THE LIVING THAMES
The Restoration of a Great Tidal River

Windsor Castle, seen across the Thames

THE LIVING THAMES
The Restoration of a Great Tidal River

John Doxat

Hutchinson Benham, London

By the same author

Stirred – Not Shaken: The Dry Martini

Hutchinson Benham Limited
3 Fitzroy Square London W1

An imprint of the Hutchinson Publishing Group

London Melbourne Sydney Auckland Wellington
Johannesburg and agencies
throughout the world

First Published 1977
© Thames Water Authority 1977

Photo typeset in Plantin

Printed in Great Britain by Grillford Limited Milton Keynes
and bound by Wm Brendon and Son Ltd Tiptree, Essex

Photographs, unless otherwise credited,
by Photographic Techniques Ltd

ISBN 0 09 129641 2

CONTENTS

By gracious permission, the author respectfully dedicates this book on the preservation of the Royal River Thames to H.R.H. The Prince Philip, Duke of Edinburgh, whose active interest in conservation has proved so important a reinforcement to all who are concerned with preservation of the environment
ANNO DOMINI 1977

FOREWORD

Those who think of the tidal Thames only as the foul river it once was, or who have seen many of the world's urban waterways reduced to little more than vast drains, should rejoice at the story so ably described in the following pages. The author explains, in an immensely readable way, how London's enormous expansion led to the river's tragic decline, and describes the remarkable transformation undertaken in the past few years.

It has been my great good fortune to be associated with the Thames for many years, and to have seen its rebirth at first hand. I might even claim, with some justification, to have been among the midwives on that happy occasion. Few things give me more pleasure than now seeing regular fishing on stretches of river that even Eels could not live in twenty years ago. In the 1950s, the river was completely devoid of oxygen, and fish put into the water would literally choke to death. Today, we have over ninety species recorded in the Tideway and more are confidently predicted. Admittedly some, like the Seahorse and the Chinese Mitten Crab, are just exotic visitors, although none the less welcome, but the Smelt, for example, are true inhabitants of the river, and are among the fish upon which a major fishery, feeding London's earlier population, was founded.

The decline in the Thames was tragic but inevitable. London, like most major cities, grew much faster than could have been anticipated by the original inhabitants. It grew much faster than contemporary technology could cope with. Planning in its modern sense was rarely practised, and London, particularly during the period of the industrial revolution, swallowed vast amounts of the surrounding countryside. This countryside included many pleasant streams that had flowed to the Thames uninterrupted for centuries, supplying surrounding villages with comparatively clean water, and supporting a wide variety of fish and animal life. These streams quickly became no more than open sewers.

It is the record of this ever-accelerating pollution gradually choking the river to death, and the public determination that brought it back to life, that forms the major part of this book. The roles played by industry and public authorities both in causing and solving the problems are covered concisely and impartially.

As a result of their efforts we may now look upon a river which is perhaps the cleanest metropolitan estuary in the world. It doesn't always look very clean, of course, but the strong tidal sweep of the river constantly lifting mud and sand from the bottom, gives that rich brown look we are becoming used to. Take a sample anywhere in the Tideway, let it stand for thirty minutes or so, and you'll have something which *looks* clean enough to drink.

The Thames has always played a major part in London's history and was, for many years, the city's main highway. Inevitably there have been many books about the river, but this is the first to record its rebirth. It contains no heroics or epic deeds. It is a record of vision, dedication and plain hard work, and one that everyone in this country should read with pride.

The occasion for this publication is fitting. By far the greater part of the improvement described in the book has been achieved during the reign of Her Majesty Queen Elizabeth II. It is wholly apt to add to the wealth of Jubilee celebrations this account of the saving of what is essentially the Royal River.

PETER BLACK
Chairman, Thames Water Authority

AUTHOR'S PREFACE

As an adolescent, I went to France to live with a French family. Their attitude to water made an immediate impression on me. The supply was metered. Though the household was fairly comfortably placed, water for bathing and household purposes was treated with marked respect: it was costly, and severe economy ruled its use. Yet the same fluid, as a potable, was suspect. It was deeply distrusted, through a legacy of once fully justified fear. Before I left London I had been warned never to drink French tap water, a by then unfounded travellers' tradition. Coming from metropolitan Britain, where for many decades water had been pure, copious and inexpensive, in my insular way I found it extraordinary that water could be both precious and despised. Nor were my hosts' drains quite up to my fastidious standards. I had taken for granted an unlimited water supply, and magnificent sewage disposal, which were indeed the envy of, and example to, many other countries – even if Americans said our domestic plumbing was deplorable! Most of our European neighbours have now caught up with us.

I intrude this minor personal memoir because I feel it illustrates a complacency still shared by many in this country. Only when affected by extreme drought do town-dwellers consider whence comes the water that we use with growing profligacy. Virtually never do we give consideration to how our noxious waste is disposed. That it is in no way a political issue may explain some of this lack of interest; it has been said, 'there are no votes in sewage'.

To move from the general to the particular, we come to the purpose of this little book. Only peripherally does it concern water supply. It does deal with pollution, environment, amenities, ecology – vogue words which can become mere jargon but to which I hope to give sound meaning within my context.

Our subject is the Thames, and mainly a special part of the Thames – the tidal river that stretches from Teddington to the North Sea. Fed by the sweet upper river, invaded by the distant ocean, this Tideway has historically been London's lifeline, and remains vital to the capital's existence. But it has not always been London's pride.

Happily, this is a success story, of which Londoners, and the millions who visit London, are largely unaware. The time is ripe to give credit to the brilliant work of dedicated men – active, retired or deceased. I shall also show, in an age when it is not always easy so to do, that bureaucracy can be alive to simple human interests as well as to more mundane issues. From reams of history, from massive technical reports, I hope to disinter – and explain briefly in lay terms – what has been done to allow Londoners the enjoyment of their river again, an enjoyment which will increase as plans for the future eventuate.

I am flattered that my work should be introduced by so distinguished a public figure as Mr Peter Black, Chairman of the Thames Water Authority. Over the years, in his capacity as member of the Thames Conservancy Board, the Metropolitan Water Board, the Port of London Authority and of the Greater London Council (where he has served as Chairman) and as chairman of the Public Services Committee, he more than anyone else has been the moving spirit behind the rejuvenation of the Thames.

1 HISTORICAL PERSPECTIVE

Glide gently, thus for ever glide
Oh Thames! that other bards may see
As lovely visions by thy side
As now, fair river, come to me.
WILLIAM WORDSWORTH (1770-1850)
'On Westminster Bridge'

The River and its Region

The Thames takes its name from the Latin *Tamesis*, and that is the name given it on early maps of London. Conjecturally, *Tam* is archaic for 'wide' or 'broad', whilst *esis* or *isis* – elsewhere surviving as *esk, ouse, ex* – has its roots in the ancient Celtic *uisg(e)* (water), from which derives also whisky (*uisge-beatha*: water of life). Hence, logically, a confluence of the isis (*esis*) and a broad (*tam*) river became latinized to *Tam-esis*. The Thame, like the Isis, is a tributary of the Thames. Whatever the etymology, and despite some localized names on upper reaches, topographically from Cricklade to the sea the river we know is the Thames.

Offically, the source is Thames Head, three miles south from Cheltenham and about as far from the great River Severn, which some call Britains's longest. However, the exact length of a river is uncertain, and somewhat dependent on regional pride. In his splendid *London's River*, Philip

Howard surprisingly gives the palm to the Severn.
As a Londoner, I'll back the Chambers Encyclopaedia
(1879) in saying that the Thames is longer, by 35
miles, than the 215 miles it is granted by that most
gifted of Thamesmen, Sir Alan Herbert.

So far as history goes, it is not the pleasing upper
reaches which count for much. The river was
known outside Britain in pre-Roman times, and
must have played some part in opening up south-
east England to continental trade. Yet, if one com-
pares it to, say, the Euphrates, the Thames is a
newcomer in historical terms. The Thames's history began only when Julius Caesar crossed it in
54 B.C. – probably at Brentford but possibly at
Westminster. Stakes have been found in the river
at Brentford which may be part of the British under-
water defences which Caesar mentioned in his com-
mentary on his second invasion. He went on to
defeat Cassivellaunus near St Albans. But Caesar
did not consolidate his victories. Nearly a century
was to elapse before Claudius set the style for Roman
conquest and colonization. The Romans made St
Albans (Verulamium) their capital, and their first
road – to connect that city with Dover – almost
certainly crossed the Thames by the marshes at
Westminster. Hence London (Londinium) became
an early focal point of Roman civilization. From
then dated the importance of the Thames, concen-
rated on London and the lower reaches. I shall deal
with this when I write about the tidal river that is
my main theme.

The renown of the Thames, as has often been re-
marked, is out of all relation to its proportions or
grandeur. It is a mere stream compared to the
Amazon, Mississippi or Nile . . . It lacks the glories
of the Rhine, the power of the Danube, the mystique
of the Ganges . . . Scenically, Scotland's Dee far ex-
cels it . . . . Yet in many ways the Thames is in-
comparable. It is as familiar a name as that of any
river in the world. Its short length is compensated
by the fact that a fifth of Britain's population live

within its watershed. It made possible the growth of London, which, as we shall see, nearly killed that which had made it mighty. From the Thames, more than any single location, the power of Britain forged, and for long controlled, the greatest empire known to man. That empire has gone, as all empires do, but its reflected glory unconsciously illuminates the river in the minds of millions who have never seen it. Only one other imperial river, the also physically insignificant Tiber, attracted the prefix Father.

The Thames basin is an agricultural and industrial region. It is also a vital source of water, houses a major port, and has widespread recreational uses. The catchment area covers some 5000 square miles, 60 per cent of the population of which are in Greater London. The whole of this now comes within the scope of the Thames Water Authority, which effectively controls the river and its tributaries, excluding navigation in the estuary. Navigation, from Teddington to the Nore — which is well out to sea but where the Thames legally ends — remains in the control of the Port of London Authority.

The extent of the Thames region may not be fully appreciated even by some of its inhabitants. It

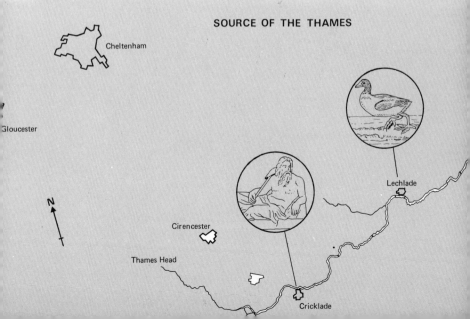

SOURCE OF THE THAMES

is obvious to citizens of Oxford or Reading, or Gravesend on the estuary, but do households in Banbury or Luton, in Basingstoke or Guildford appreciate that they, too, enormously depend on the vast network under the jurisdiction of Thames Water?

I do not wish to get bogged down with statistics, yet a few basic ones are essential. The daily water requirements of the region currently run at an *average* 925 million gallons a day. The source of half this water is the Thames itself or tributaries: the Lea, the major river joining the Tideway from the north side, contributes over 7 per cent of the total and is considered a separate source. Most of the remainder comes from underground: there is also some re-use. Direct abstraction is licensed in certain areas: of this, 50 per cent is taken by the Central Electricity Generating Board and 5 per cent by agriculture. Of the rest of the water supplied, 75 per cent is unmetered and mainly for domestic use, and 25 per cent is for metered, industrial puposes. Though dispersal of industry is somewhat reducing its requirements, ever increasing standards of living – washing-machines for instance – involve yearly enhanced demands in the domestic sector.

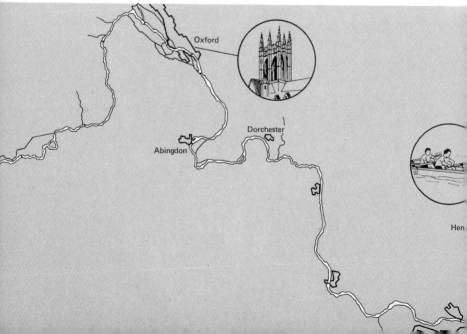

During the drought of 1976 pumps were installed at Molesey Weir to make the Thames flow backwards. This helped fill reservoirs upstream

THE UPPER REACHES

N

Marlow

Maidenhead

Eton

Windsor

Runymede Staines

Reading

Brentford

Chis

Isleworth Kew Ba

Richmo
Sheen

Twickenham

Teddington

East
Molesey

Kings

Hamp
Court

Chelsea Reservoir, Molesey, during the summer of 1976

Obviously, the Thames basin is of supreme national importance. Some 12 million people depend on it for water and use its sewerage facilities – that is, confide in it for basic health. An unknown number of millions directly or indirectly rely for work on manufacturing and commerce nurtured by the river. The Tideway itself contains such a concentration of people and activities as to present continuing problems, historic, actual and of the future.

Rainfall excesses are a constant preoccupation of the Authority; drainage is the converse of supply of

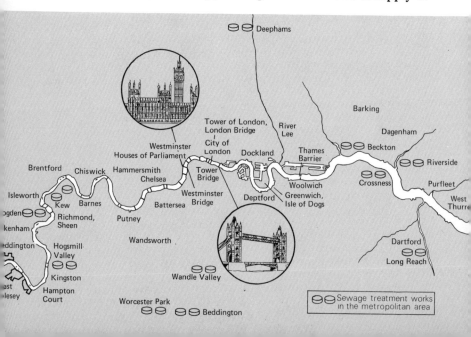

water. The 1976 drought – greatly mitigated in London by far-sightedness – will not quickly be forgotten. Less remembered is such an event as that of 15 August 1975, when, during a heat wave which had baked the ground, 6¾ inches of rain fell in a day in Hampstead round a radius of six miles. Only inundations of such literally record proportions cause serious damage or dislocation: the responsibility for guarding against them is part of the Authority's very varied activities. Surface water disposal goes hand in hand with sewerage: I deal with that subject – absolutely vital to pollution control – at some length elsewhere.

An indication of emergencies that can crop up, with which the Authority must cope as part of its work within the Thames basin, was the spillage in Ealing of 5000 gallons of petrol. Despite prompt local action, a considerable quantity of volatile spirit flowed into drains, filling sewers with explosive vapour. By rapid diversion of water, within twenty-four hours this had been flushed away, and a potential catastrophe had been avoided without any unnecessary public alarm. These emergencies call for intense co-operation between the Water Authority and other organizations, which is invariably forthcoming.

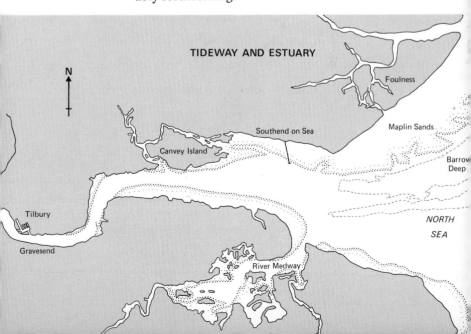

Also involving possible detonation, though infinitely less risky, was the discovery of unexploded bombs during the draining, for maintenance purposes, of a great reservoir at Staines in 1976. At the same time here was uncovered a motor car – stolen in 1951!

Peculiar circumstances sometimes arise, such as the pop festival at the disused R A F airfield at Shrivenham, Oxfordshire. In short order, drinking water was laid on for 20 000 people – though only 10 000 attended – and because of the possible contamination of the ground, arrangements were made for tankering all sewage for treatment elsewhere. A health hazard was thus quietly obviated. These few examples are mentioned to show the eternal and diverse vigilance required to protect the Thames region.

For the Thames is not just a river: it is the life-blood of a major region of Britain. It is more than that: it is part of the nation's heritage.

The Upper Reaches

There are almost as many books about the Thames as there are about love.

SIR ALAN HERBERT (1890-1971), *The Thames*

The Tideway, our principal concern, is largely fed by the non-tidal river, stretching from the source to Teddington, where is the lowest lock on the river. The upper river has played a crucial role in preserving the Thames, and if success was achieved upstream earlier, it was because of this success that the whole endangered river has been saved.

The upper reaches, like the tidal portion, were once in serious peril. In the past, the greatest problem was flooding. For centuries, the upper Thames was bordered by lush water meadows, rich arable land, and small prosperous villages and towns, drawing their water from it and from time immemorial putting their waste into it, without affecting the age-old balance of nature. The river was also a traditional highway, though traffic moved very slowly owing to the succession of weirs and the consequent laborious porterage around them. With the introduction of locks, which eventually allowed unimpeded barge transport from the sea to Lechlade, villages became towns and towns evolved into cities. Riverside industry burgeoned in such places as Reading and almost engulfed Oxford. As often happens with improvements, the locks, by impeding free flow, themselves compounded the bad effects of the expansion they brought with them.

The upper reaches of the Thames have a timeless quality

Fortunately, Victorian *laissez-faire* did not permit pollution of the upper Thames to get out of hand. But it was a near call.

In 1857 the Thames Conservancy Board was formed, and a vigorous and successful organization it turned out to be. Yet, despite the energetic attitude of the Conservators, their initial powers proved inadequate against some purse-conscious local authorities. In 1865, it was necessary to appoint a 'Select Committee on the River Thames'. It reported (in relation to the upper reaches): 'It was proved to your Committee that the discharge of sewage has of late become a serious impediment to navigation, as at times the accumulation of solid matter is so great in the locks that it has to be removed at considerable expense, and delay occurs before the lock gates can be opened.' Pollution by sewage was the river's principal danger, but it is interesting to note the contemporary emphasis on loss to commerce rather than on cost in amenities or to health.

The Conservators' original mandate did not extend upstream above Staines. As a result of the Select Committee's report, in 1866 this was extended to Cricklade. The following year the Conservancy was given control of the first three miles up any tributaries and later this was extended to ten miles. The Conservators wasted no time in unleashing their enhanced authority. They ordered towns to cease discharging sewage into the river. They controlled the amount of water that could be abstracted. They did not hesitate to prosecute delinquents, civic, agricultural, private or industrial – even if the Courts did not always side with them. In 1866 alone, seventy-seven industrial firms were prosecuted for permitting polluting waste to enter the river, and nine towns – including Oxford, Reading, Henley, Eton and Windsor – were served with notices ordering them to stop putting sewage into the Thames. By 1874, above Surbiton – where there was an important intake of water for domestic use – only Oxford, Abingdon, Reading and Windsor were still offending. Smaller communities paid much more attention to the Conservators.

Not until 1880 did Oxford have comprehensive sewerage: almost within living memory mediaeval conditions of sanitation prevailed in many quarters of the ancient University city and epidemics were frequent: *mens sana,* perhaps, but not *in corpore sano!*

In 1867 cholera was still endemic in Reading: it was another eight years before satisfactory sewerage was introduced. In Windsor, parts of the borough had sewers prior to 1850, the crude sewage going straight into the river at three points. After cholera outbreaks, these sewers were re-directed to a single point downstream from the town – which pleased the citizens, if not the Conservators. A new scheme, involving modern chemical treatment, was belatedly started in 1874. This was the first of its type in the country and became widely admired by visiting experts from overseas for its salubrity and lack of odour.

Kingston, reputedly an ancient capital of England, was another major centre of riverside population which caused trouble. In 1888, the borough gave in to progress and initiated a novel sewage treatment plant, operated by a firm named the Native Guano Company, which ingeniously managed to sell powdered sludge for the then considerable sum of £3 10s. (£3.50) per ton.

These examples are mentioned to indicate the effort required by the Thames Conservancy to save the fresh-water Thames from the disaster that so nearly overwhelmed the Tideway. Nowadays about 220 million gallons of treated effluent daily enter the upper Thames and its tributaries, in all some 2400 miles of waterways. As much as 1300 million gallons a day may be taken out for domestic use. Pollution is virtually non-existent: the oxygen level is high. Fish abound; safe bathing in summer is popular in many places. It has been claimed that angling and boating (in every form) are more widely practised on the Thames than on any similar river in Britain, perhaps in the world. Personally, I can vouch

'Thames raters' skim the surface at Bourne End. More than 30 000 craft of all types are registered with the Thames Water Authority

for the pleasures of holidaying by boat on the upper reaches and for the excellence of the facilities provided by the Thames Water Authority which, in 1974, took over the Conservators' fine heritage and which now guards the river with equal zeal. Sensible restrictions are strictly applied as to speed limits and sanitation: flush WCs on pleasure craft must be rendered inoperative and chemical toilets alone are permitted which must be cleansed at regularly placed installations. Throwing rubbish into the river is a serious offence.

The fresh-water Thames is a gentle river. There are no dramatic views. Close to London the water can be as busy with craft as Piccadilly Circus with cars. Yet even here there are quiet backwaters, quaint boat-yards, individualistic communities of river-dwellers, riverside pubs which are a very British aspect of the scene. There are many Thames – each with its own atmosphere and charm. History often greets one – Runnymede, proud Windsor, the Tudor magnificence of Hampton Court, the fabled spires of Oxford (before you see the factories) . . . .

The Thames as a water playground: canoeing at Abingdon

Upstream, for miles at a time one can imagine oneself in an idyllic rural England of before the industrial revolution. Each Thames-lover has his own preference. For many, the non-tidal Thames is best above bustling Maidenhead. You may choose serene Henley (except at Regatta time), or push on as far as Lechlade. But let me rest at Marlow (now mercifully by-passed from polluting traffic), popularly, if inaccurately, associated with Isaak Walton, author of *The Compleat Angler,* that gem of contemplative literature. I thought of him as I spent a glorious holiday, quite alone, in a boat-house by Bisham Abbey, and, taking out a skiff at first light, in the misty dawn, I saw a patient fisherman reverentially take a huge carp from the still water. We murmured greetings as he weighed his catch and gently slipped it back into the stream. Such delights are only possible because over a century ago some far-sighted men decided to save the river for posterity; their successors, at the Thames Water Authority, quietly continue the good work. Until recently I did not appreciate this. My water rates are the only tax I now pay with a promptness that is tinged with gratitude!

The Tidal River

Every drop of the Thames is liquid history.

JOHN BURNS, pioneer dockers' union leader
(1858-1943)

If I have been somewhat dismissive of the upper Thames, it is because my brief is to concentrate on the Tideway. Here the river assumes a fresh role and a new importance enhanced by the great improvements that it is my purpose to recount. So we will embark on a brief imaginary voyage that will take us from Kingston to the coast.

Though at Teddington is the official demarcation between tidal and non-tidal, the lowest impassable barrier for fish occurs at Molesey. There was no mechanized weir at Teddington until 1912.

The official flow of the fresh-water Thames is measured – and controlled – at Teddington weir; the average is rather under 1500 million gallons per day – but it varies enormously with the seasons.

Kingston, still noted for its market, was a major centre in ancient times, commercially and administratively. It provided one of two safe fords across the Thames above Westminster and for long there was no bridge below Kingston until one got to London Bridge. There was a bridge at Kingston in the twelfth century. The earliest written record concerning Kingston dates from 838: in that year, the first man to declare himself King of England – instead of just some part of it – held a Council at what was then called Cyningestun.

The area's Royal associations are abundant. Though built by Cardinal Wolsey, Hampton Court soon passed to Henry VIII: five of his consorts resided – if sometimes briefly – at Hampton Court.

Apart from its proximity to Royal Richmond and good river-borne transport to London, one reason why Wolsey built where he did was the salubrity of the well-drained location. Yet the Cardinal would not touch the water of the river by his vast palace. Lead pipes brought his water from springs three miles away on the other side of the Thames.

Below Teddington the Thames Conservancy – dating from 1857 – relinquished control of navigation to the Port of London Authority, created in 1909. To this body, and much more to the Greater London Council and latterly to the Thames Water Authority, is due the revival of the river. From Teddington to Richmond it is still fairly rustic; the houses do not much intrude and many add architectural beauty to the scene. Industry is not intrusive. The quaintly named eyots or aits – little islands – break up the channel: they are havens for river folk, many of whom live permanently on the water and give rise to a minor pollution problem. Others appear to spend more time 'making ready' – painting, polishing, repairing – than actually putting their craft into motion. Yet in summer the water teems with boats, as it has for centuries.

Pleasing Twickenham is, like Kingston, a settlement of great antiquity. No Royal connection, however, brought it to prominence. Its riverine peace attracted literary figures, notably the acerbic Alexander Pope. But better remembered locally is Horace Walpole, for at Twickenham he constructed – rather reconstructed – Strawberry Hill, epitome of the Gothic Revival in architecture. On this masterpiece Walpole spent thirty years from 1747.

Richmond is as far upriver as many Londoners ever travel. The unspoilt view from Richmond Hill is as famous and and lovely as any in England. No feat of imagination is required to re-live such events as the Richmond dinner party expedition in the *Forsyte Saga*, when Montague Dartie made such a nuisance of himself.

The Richmond reach was recorded as a notable fishing ground in 1577 – and there is good reason for it to become so again. Doubtless these fish provided

November 1974 saw very high water levels on the Thames. Here flood water is passing through six of the thirty-four radial gates at Teddington Weir

fare for Royalty: from the reign of Henry I, Richmond and Royalty have gone together. If the Thames achieves Royal status at Windsor, at Richmond – formerly Shene (Sheen) – it becomes positively Regal. Richard II's Shene palace had such conveniencies as proper toilets and hot and cold water laid on: not since the Romans left had such adjuncts to good living been known in England. It was Henry VII who gave the town its name, since he was Earl of Richmond, Yorkshire. It was on *that* hill where lived the lass 'more bright than May Day morn'. Elizabeth I died in Richmond Palace, and it remained a favoured residence of the Sovereign until the 'Farmer King', George III, moved to Kew.

Below Richmond, the river begins to lose its rural complexion on the left bank, still referred to as Middlesex side though Middlesex was abolished, except postally, in 1965. Middlesex derives from *middel seaxon*, or middle Saxons, who lived between the West Saxons (Wessex), East Saxons (Essex), and South Saxons (Sussex).

The river from
Richmond Hill

Middlesex was historically the market garden of the capital. At Isleworth, famous for fruit, salmon were plentiful until the early nineteenth century. In 1848, a report stated, 'Salmon have been driven from the river by the gas-works and steam navigation'. Brentford had one of the first major gas-works in Britain. The Company's chairman was Sir Felix Booth, who, in the same town, had a large brewery and gin distillery. Industrialization of the riverside, well upstream from London proper, grew apace — to the detriment of the river. Today, considerable improvements are taking place to restore the Thames-side around Brentford. Hard by is magnificent Syon House, for three and a half centuries the seat of the Dukes of Northumberland and remarkable amongst private palaces in the London region in being in family occupation. Typical of aristocratic enterprise in our stringent times, Syon Park houses one of the first, and amongst the largest, garden centres in the country. It is appropriate that this garden centre should by sited in grounds landscaped by that greatest of all English professional gardeners, 'Capability' Brown. Syon's gardens were planned on the heroic scale; there are six acres of roses alone.

Now we revert to the right bank.

Since this is no more than an introduction to the riverside delights and peculiarities of the London Thames, I must perforce neglect many places, such as Marble Hill and Eel Pie Island, in favour of better-known features, like Kew Gardens. These house the world's greatest collection of plants – living or dried – and a fantastic botanical library.

It was George II's consort, Queen Caroline, who laid out the first gardens at Kew. George III moved to Kew after the death of his mother, Augusta, the Dowager Princess of Wales. He could there indulge in the simple family life he preferred to the Court luxuries for which his heir (Prince Regent, later George IV) was to show such predilection. When the latter came to the throne, Kew's royal connection declined though the gardens were enlarged during Queen Victoria's reign: they now exceed three hundred acres.

We next come to a part of the river which is perhaps more famous as the setting for the Oxford and Cambridge Boat Race than any other single reason. The Chiswick to Putney section is much given to water sports. The left bank at Chiswick has some beautiful riverside houses, walks – and several fine pubs. On the right bank one can walk pleasurably from Barnes to Putney which, as a rowing centre, almost rivals Henley at weekends. The water is clean enough but there remains some hazard from floating timber which finds its way upstream from the Pool of London. Regulations designed to decrease air pollution by banning unauthorized bonfires, increased flotsam in the river, since a lot of this wood used to be incinerated on the mudbanks.

We are now truly in London and industry becomes increasingly apparent, particularly around Wandsworth, named for the part-hidden Wandle River, whose angling merits, before it was covered, were lauded by Isaak Walton: it's a very different Wandsworth today.

At Chelsea, the Thames assumes a metropolitan aspect, fully tamed between embankments as it ebbs and flows with dignity through the heart of the capital. Here is the tourist's Thames, the Thames commemorated on millions of postcards, the Thames above which Big Ben booms the hours. As the river sweeps past the Houses of Parliament and on to the City of London, it offers views that never fail to enchant visitors, make Londoners proud and haunt the memory of exiles. Here, at the nub of London, the Thames is grand but never pompous. There are intimate, almost homely, touches: against the controversial backdrop of a starkly rebuilt South Bank, it does not seem incongruous that moored alongside the north embankment are such assorted vessels as a pub, fashioned from an old paddle steamer; Captain Scott's Antarctic ship, *Discovery;* a floating (Spanish) restaurant; the only water-borne City Livery Hall — the Master Mariners' . . . . Successors to the state barges of yore, launches ply from Westminster up and down stream.

London Bridge is now a location rather than a structure: I, for one, cannot take the modern bridge seriously. The one that it replaced now incongruously stands in Arizona, spanning an artificial New Thames. But it is the oft-pictured medieval London Bridge, replete with houses — and traitors' heads — that remains London Bridge for most people. For centuries 'London Bridge' has been the spot where tides are measured.

Then comes the Tower of London whence Henry VIII's polar bear was led to fish in the river — for salmon, of course!

Once past the City we enter the Pool and Dockland, dead or dying as the shipping traffic moves increasingly to the estuary and Tilbury. Eastwards, only Greenwich reminds us of the Thames in the hey-day of regal glory, its superb architecture shaming the new town of Thamesmead.

From Barking on, it is nearly all industry and mud, with little scenic delight — though there is increasingly much to excite the bird-watcher. History

The Houses of Parliament, from the Albert Embankment

briefly erupts at Gravesend where in 1617 "Princess" Pocohontas died young and forgotten by Society which had at first been enraptured by her. Later, her legend became entrenched in Anglo-American folklore and her "descendants" are legion.

The trickle which started in Gloucestershire, and burgeoned into the great Thames, as last prepares to lose itself in the North Sea. It spreads. Tilbury is an ocean terminal. Southend is technically on a river but its suffix is "On Sea". Marshes attract abundant bird life. Commuter colonies flourish. Fishing smacks toil. Sailing boats dot the water like giant seagulls. An occasional sprit-sail barge, relic of a once mighty fleet, picturesquely lumbers across the horizon...

Father Thames bids goodbye to the land he waters and drains.

2 A RIVER IN DANGER

On Thames's bank in silent thought we stood,
Where Greenwich smiles upon the silver flood;
Pleased with the seat which gave Eliza birth, *
We kneel and kiss the consecrated earth.

SAMUEL JOHNSON (1709-1784), *London*

When visiting the site of the Temple of Mithras in
the city of London, during extensive archaeological
excavations which preceded the covering of numerous ancient ruins by an enormous office block, my
guide – who was more concerned with modern construction than historical reconstruction – pointed
out a deep deposit of old oyster shells. They had been
discarded from the kitchens of an adjacent Roman
villa, whose foundations were visible. Most of the
shells crumbled to the touch, but a few had fossilized:
I had one mounted and gave it to Mr Bill Bentley, of
West End oyster bar fame, as a 2000-year-old memorial to the fact that once the Thames ran so limpidly
that oysters – bivalves notoriously pernickety about
their environment – formerly thrived.

The Romans relished oysters, crustaceans and
fishes, in which the Thames was rich. They also
knew a great deal about storing, filtering and trans-
porting water, as well as effective disposal of waste
products. When the Romans withdrew, barbarism
succeeded civilization – in sanitation as in much
else. Yet the martyrdom of London's river still lay in
the future. For centuries the capital's growth was
slow. But gradually the purity of the tidal Thames
was being sullied.

* Queen Elizabeth I was born at Greenwich on 7 September 1533

At an early date the dangers were partially realized. From the thirteenth century are recorded instances of Crown and City endeavouring to restrict the use of the river as a sewer and rubbish dump. It was not customary to pay much attention to such edicts. However, the population was small enough, and the tides usually strong enough, for nature to handle the situation fairly adequately.

The Thames-side London that Canaletto painted gloriously straddled a river still so healthy that a thriving fishing industry was centred on Billingsgate. Most of us have heard of the London apprenticēs' plea that they be not served salmon so often. Oysters could be had for a penny a dozen.

The population of greater London doubled between 1700 and 1820, to around 1 250 000. Human waste came to present problems exceeding traditional methods of disposal. Existing sewers were designed

Left: The Fleet River near St Pancras in 1825. Today the Fleet flows completely underground from Hampstead to Blackfriars Bridge

A view of the Fleet from the 'Red Lion' in 1844, showing the chutes from the houses discharging into the stream.
The Mansell Collection

only to take away surface water. It was forbidden to put any household or industrial waste into them, a prohibition far from strictly observed. The contents of cesspools, individual or communal, were principally removed at intervals to fertilize the land, a residue finding its way into the Thames. Then came a proliferation of efficient water-closets – not themselves a new invention, but hitherto a perquisite of the wealthier citizens. The cesspools became congested, and this could only be solved by overflows, connected to open street sewers whose noisome burden found its way to the Thames. For a time, the obliging river coped. But the final contamination of the Thames was under way. Sewer-tributaries, like the famous Fleet River, developed into odiferous open drains.

The new Metropolitan Commissioners of Sewers, established in 1843, unwittingly provided a crucial

MICROCOSM dedicated to the London Water Companies

MONSTER SOUP commonly called THAMES WATER being a correct representation of that precious stuff doled out to us

'MICROCOSM
dedicated to the
London Water
Companies.'
'MONSTER SOUP
commonly called
THAMES WATER
being a correct
representation of that
precious stuff doled
out to us.' A cartoon
by Paul Pry, 1829.
*Courtesy Royal
Institute of Chemists*

challenge to the salubrity of the Tideway. With the admirable object of improving appalling sanitation in the horrendous poor quarters of London, they abolished some 200 000 individual cesspools – source of constant infection – and compulsorily attached these households and tenements to main sewers. These drained directly into the Thames. The land's loss in fertilizer was the river's gain in suffocated fish and suffocating riverside residents. The human and industrial effluvia of a metropolis expanding at a sensational rate poured into the tidal basin, polluting it beyond the point where it could scour itself clean. Foul excreta-soaked mud festered on the flats at low tide, and, at the flood, horrible muck was borne upstream in ever-increasing loads. The courageous river had to resign the uneven battle. Fish barely survived; birds began to retreat.

The cholera epidemics of 1831-2 were repeated in 1848-9, when 14 000 fatalities occurred. Between then and 1855 six Commissions tackled the problem of the menaced Thames. None could arrive at a

FARADAY GIVING HIS CARD TO FATHER THAMES;
And we hope the Dirty Fellow will consult the learned Professor.

A comment by *Punch* on Faraday's open letter about the state of the Thames, July 1885

solution. In 1855, the Metropolitan Board of Works was founded. One of its prime objects was to halt the involuntary destruction by three million Londoners of their own river. Multiplying and virtually uncontrolled industry added its own quota of pollution.

Joseph (later Sir Joseph) Bazalgette – best remembered by the public for his engineering of the Victoria Embankment, which is one souvenir of his genius and which carries his actual memorial – had prepared for the Board of Works a comprehensive sewerage scheme. This was ready by 1856, known as the Year of the Big Stink – though others rivalled it. The condition of the Thames had become critical. A year previously, the great Michael

Faraday, father of electrical technology, had felt impelled to write to *The Times* about a boat journey between Hungerford (Charing Cross) and London bridges: 'The whole of the river was an opaque pale brown fluid. . . . Near the bridges the feculence [putrefaction] rolled up in clouds so dense that they were visible at the surface.'

The Bazalgette plan was held up by legislative delays until 1858, when a hot summer 'created as much anxiety in the public mind as did the revolt in India [the Indian Mutiny] last year', to quote a London newspaper. An M P said: 'By perverse ingenuity, one of the noblest of rivers has been changed into a cesspool.'

In the Upper House, a peer echoed popular opinion when he stated that the Thames had become 'a most abominable ditch'. Sheets drenched in disinfectant had to be hung in the House of Commons in ineffective effort to dispel the prevailing stench. Conditions were just as bad in 1859, and a journal found some satisfaction that the suppurating river 'flowed under Parliament's own wise nose'.

Once approved, Sir Joseph's ideas were pressed forward with the speed and thoroughness that characterised Victorian enterprise, civic or private. To put it simply, the metropolis was to be by-passed by means of three main sewers on the north bank and two on the south. Into these would drain existing and supplementary sewers. Instead of flowing into the Thames as it passed through central London, the city's sewage was to be directed to outfalls at Barking on the north and Crossness to the south — both over ten miles downstream from London Bridge. The sewage was untreated. It was stored in vast reservoirs which were emptied on the ebb tide, the notion being that it would be carried to sea and dissolved by the kindly waves.

This enormously ambitious scheme was mainly completed in 1865 and opened with appropriate pomp by the Prince of Wales. Such was the quality of construction that many vital sewers then built are satisfactorily in use today.

Opening the main metropolitan drainage works at Crossness in April 1865, the Prince of Wales starts the engines. *The Illustrated London News*

Most of the occasional horrors experienced by dwellers in low-lying – and some not so low-lying – parts of London were gradually obviated. However, the inhabitants of the estuary, in the vicinity of the outfalls, were decidedly less happy. Not for well over a further decade was large-scale and effective treatment of the sewage applied.

Despite new techniques, London's growth exerted constant pressure on sewerage. In 1880 the population was 4¾ millions: by 1939, it was 8¼ millions. Apart from the great downstream sewage works, over 180 others were discharging effluent into the Thames and its tributaries within twenty-five miles of the capital's heart. Pioneer improvements, outlined elsewhere, had been made to these discharges, and at least it could be claimed that the tidal Thames was no longer totally polluted. However, it was a long way from a perfect river. No fish could live in it except as a freakish rarity: oxygen levels of the water were nil, or very low. Birds shunned reaches where once they thronged. One need not be at all old to recall summers when a towpath walk could be a mixed pleasure. Though the worst was in the past, into the 1960s the river could still turn rancid.

In the continuing fight to save London's Thames –and restore it to something akin to the pristine purity of Roman times – giant strides remained to be taken. As we shall see, they were.

3 THE THAMES SAVED

From Sewage to Sweet Water

Forget six counties overhung with smoke,
Forget the snorting steam and piston stroke,
Forget the spreading of the hideous town;
Think rather of the pack-horse on the down,
And dream of London, small and white and clean,
The clear Thames bordered by its gardens green.

WILLIAM MORRIS (1834-1896), *The Earthly Paradise*

In 1861 typhoid fever killed Queen Victoria's Prince Albert. Its cause was almost certainly infected old drains at Windsor Castle, allied to primitive local sewerage into the adjacent Thames. Ironically, he was a man dedicated to progress and civic improvement. A little over a century ago, the mighty hardly less than the man in the street daily risked diseases brought on by ineffective public hygiene.

I interpolate this historic Royal fatality to emphasize how rotten was sanitation in fairly recent times, in a very inventive era, and beside the comparatively uncontaminated upper Thames. Worse, of course, were conditions on the Tideway. Before dealing with modern efforts that have restored the river to a nigh miraculous extent, it is pertinent to revert to Sir Joseph Bazalgette. Though he improved

Above: Abbey Mills Pumping Station, opened by Sir John Thwaites in 1868

An interior view of the main engine house at Abbey Mills, showing two of the electric motors which drive centrifugal pumps

Construction of the Wick branch line of the northern outfall sewer; from *The Illustrated London News,* 27 August 1859. This sectional view shows the tunnels raised above ground level. *G L C Print Collection*

he could not cure the Thames. Yet to his plans we owe the river's present salubrity. Though perhaps less remembered than his contemporary, Isambard Kingdom Brunel, this superb and far-sighted engineer probably did more good, and saved more lives, than any single Victorian public official. On his firm foundations rests our Thames's wholesomeness.

Five years before Prince Albert's death, Sir Joseph had prepared his giant project: in 1858 an Act of Parliament implemented it. Construction started the next year by the Metropolitan Board of Works, whose engineer was Sir Joseph, and, incidentally, whose First Commissioner was Sir Benjamin Hall, after whom the clock Big Ben is named. One hundred miles of main sewers were built, some as large as railway tunnels, and pumping stations installed at Pimlico – Buckingham Palace lies on the borders of that district – at Abbey Mills and Deptford, to urge the sewage on its way, by gravity, to Barking and Crossness. The north outfall into the Thames (Barking) and the Deptford pumping station were ready by 1864, and the south (Crossness) works received Royal inauguration the following year. The entire Bazalgette scheme was completed in 1875. Cholera and typhoid ceased to be an ever-present menace, but the condition of the river remained displeasing, to put it mildly.

In 1868,1870, and finally in 1874, the Rivers Pollution Committee recommended various treatment for sewage rather than its discharge in raw state into the Thames. Chemical treatment had been tried: it was unsatisfactory, but better than nothing. Shortly afterwards, W. J. Dibdin, later to become first Chemist for the London County Council (now Greater London Council), recommended removal of solids from sewage as the only efficient way of dealing with pollution. On his notion is based the present successful cleansing of effluents. Official reaction was slow, however. Noxious mudbanks proliferated on the lower Thames.

In 1882, a Royal Commission on Metropolitan Sewage Disposal was appointed. After ponderous deliberations it came to the rather obvious conclusion that no crude sewage should be discharged into any section of the Thames; suspended solids should in some way be separated from the liquid and these solids should be used for land reclamation or destroyed or used as fertilizer, or taken out to sea; the remaining liquid should, for the time being, be put into the river but fresh techniques for decontaminating it should be sought. Mr Dibdin put before the Commission advanced ideas on the bacteriological treatment of sewage. He was derided as a visionary: in the end he was entirely vindicated. To the detriment of the Thames, time was unnecessarily wasted.

A decision was taken to precipitate the solids in sewage at both Barking and Crossness, work commencing in 1887 and being finished two years later. Between 1887 and 1895, six sludge vessels were commissioned to take the sludge and dump it in the sea. We see the beginnings of modern London sewage treatment: yet the Thames was only reprieved. Salvation had still to be achieved

In 1889, the London County Council was formed. It took over many of the responsibilities of the Board of Works. The Council speedily recognized that ex-

General view of the southern outfall works at Crossness in 1865. *The Illustrated London News*

isting sewers were inadequate in view of the growing population and, with new and improved roads, a quicker run-off of surface water. Treatment of sewage effluent at the outfalls also caused concern. The established methods of treatment with chemicals, though known to be only partially effective, continued. Treatment through bacteria, initiated by Mr Dibdin, was researched in depth by his successor, Dr Frank Clowes, through the 1890s. At last, the practicability of large-scale biological treatment was accepted. By 1914, Manchester had triumphantly put it into practice: another instance of 'what Lancashire thinks today, London will think tomorrow'? The First World War postponed any Thames-side application.

From 1920, three types of plant for experimental biological treatment, each big enough to serve a small town, were installed at Crossness, and a major plant for 'activated sludge' processing was erected at the north outfall (Beckton) in 1928, to deal with up to 10 million gallons of sewage a day. In 1934, it was decided to erect units to bring the capacity up to 60 million gallons daily, but only partial operation had been attained when war again supervened. At the same time, exploration was going on into 'digestion of sludge' (see below) and the use of gasses produced by this. Restoration of the Thames was well in hand, but industrial and other foul effluent discharge tended to counter improvements at the two major lower Thames sewage works.

The outbreak of the Second World War faced what had become the world's largest sewage undertaking with a new threat – aerial bombardment. Damage to sewers was very extensive, but fortunately no major pumping stations were seriously hit. Though there were several near disasters by flooding and spread of untreated sewage from broken sewers, no catastrophe occurred.

Following the War, the L C C pursued its efforts to improve the quality of effluent from its sewage works. However, not until the mid-1960s did any real improvement in the quality of Thames water become apparent. Eventually, the energetic implementation of the recommendations of the Pippard Report (Chapter 4) revolutionized the situation. . . .

I stood on a wide riverside plain. No human beings were visible. As far as I could see were ranks of tanks of various design, huge concrete cylinders, big modern buildings, and the desolate shells of those grandiose brick edifices in which the Victorians gloriously enshrined their machines, confidently built to last for all time.

I was on the South bank of the Thames, at Crossness Sewage Treatment Works – synonymous with sewage disposal efficiency. There are over 450 other works, in all treating around 950 million gallons of sewage a day, serving 12 million people in the Thames Water Authority's 5000 square miles. Bazalgette would surely be proud of these successors to his pioneer feat. As president of the Institution of Civil Engineers, he said: 'The ultimate object of all sanitary science is the comfort and convenience of the living . . . .' For our purposes, that means all whose lives are touched by the purity of the Thames.

As I have elsewhere suggested, we take for granted

Above: Aerial view of
Crossness today

Raw sewage passing
through an inlet
screen

Clean effluent being
discharged into the
river at Beckton

the disposal of our sewage, the draining of our streets, as much as we do the water in our taps. I certainly did – until I toured Crossness. I would like to share this edifying experience.

I started where the sewage is screened for bits of timber, rags and so on. Larger objects have been previously extracted,. The oddest things get into main sewers, as large as old motor-bikes. What can be mechanically scraped from the screens and mashed up is so dealt with and joins the general sewage flow: intractable objects are removed and destroyed.

The sewage is now an opaque fluid, a mixture of household wastes, industrial effluent, rain water .... It contains in suspension grit and other particles which would soon harm pumps. So the fluid flows slowly by gravity through channels where the heavier solids fall to the bottom. This detritus is dredged and employed for reclamation of marshland and other filling-in jobs. There is a faintly unpleasant and pervasive odour, not strong enough to be truly offensive and un-noticed by the staff: yet I was glad my visit took place on a crisply cold day!

The sewage now goes to primary sedimentation tanks where much of the remaining solids suspended in the liquids falls to the base. This crude sludge is scraped out by ingenious machines and transferred to the 'digestion plant'. The now almost clear liquid (primary effluent) still contains polluting ingredients and is pumped to the secondary treatment plant which contains bacteria which feed on the waste matter in the sewage and thereby destroy it.

These special bacteria require copious oxygen, in which the liquid sewage is deficient. Oxygen must be induced. One way in which this is done is apparent to – if not understood by – many who have passed sewage works by train. Sewage is sprayed by rotating sprinklers on to gravel or clinker filter beds, and sufficient oxygen is taken up from the air to enliven the bacteria. However, in works the size of those at Crossness, batteries of large aerators churn the sewage; an impressive sight. After some eight hours the water is much cleaner and can safely enter the Thames, whence a proportion of it first came: from sewage to sweet water in less than half a day. In final sedimentation tanks the bacteria are recovered, to start their beneficial life-cycle again.

Meanwhile, the crude sludge is also receiving treatment in digestion tanks – towers that look like gas-holders; and are. Here the pollutants are converted by another form of bacteria into sludge-gas. This is a fairly lengthy process. This gas (akin to marsh or North Sea gas) provides a high percentage of the energy needed to run the pumps.

At Crossness, as at Beckton and other works, the quantity of 'digested sludge' produced is prodigious. It is pumped to a fleet of five ships which transport it to the seaward limits of the Thames and dump it in Barrow Deep: not actually all that deep – 60-70 feet. This sludge is very rapidly dispersed by the sea and, far from having any polluting effects, is considered to nurture some algae and thus contribute to the marine food chain and may encourage fish. In 1977, Thames Water took delivery of a replacement vessel for its sludge fleet, built by Ferguson Bros. (Port Glasgow), subsidiary of the Scott Lithgow group. Appropriately its name is *Thames*.

There are some 800 miles of main sewers in the Metropolitan Public Health Division of Thames Water alone, 400 miles of them in inner London. Additionally, there are about 14 000 miles of local sewers.

There are two basic types of sewage – surface water from roads and so on, and household and industrial liquid or semi-liquid waste. Ideally, a city should be served by two sewerages. One would funnel rain-water direct to rivers, for it is virtually uncontaminated except through occasional accident, such as oil spillage. The other would take foul sewage for treatment. Central London is served by a combination of both systems. There is no problem

other than in storm conditions, and our climate is not so extreme as currently to justify sewers constructed solely to deal with exceptional circumstances.

'Dry weather flow' to sewage works is the term loosely employed to describe normal conditions. During very heavy rain this flow is, obviously, augmented – sometimes dramatically, as in the instance of the Hampstead downpour mentioned earlier. However, the dilution of normal sewage by this accretion of water considerably reduces the concentration of pollutants. Modern treatment plants usually have the capacity to give complete treatment to up to three times their 'dry weather flow'. If the flow increased to six times normal, the surplus is diverted to reserve tanks and retained for later treatment. Flows higher than this are in most cases discharged direct into rivers: the discharge will not be of long duration and so much diluted that the river can absorb the extra load of pollutants – being in spate, it will speedily dissipate the unwanted effluents.

Aeration tanks at Beckton. In these tanks bacteria are fed with oxygen which enables them to purify the sewage – the 'activated sludge process'

Inspecting the weir in the overflow chamber at the head of the Charlton storm relief sewer

The post-war explosion in the use of detergents was a prime cause for the deteriorating condition of the Thames twenty-five years ago. Between 1951 and 1961, detergent use increased threefold. A tragic example of the results of this was when a man drowned because, though salvation was at hand, the would-be rescuers could not see him through the mass of foam.

Previously, detergents had been of vegetable origin and caused no trouble. The new 'hard' (technically, non-biodegradable) detergents contained elements which could not be degraded in the bacteriological treatment plants at sewage works. These detergents decreased the efficiency of plants by an estimated 30 per cent. So when the effluent from the works was discharged into the river it still contained much 'hard' detergent, which foamed or spread on the surface and greatly reduced the natural intake of oxygen into the water. These detergents were also toxic to fish.

The menace beame so serious that in 1957 the Standing Technical Committee on Synthetic Detergents held talks with government representatives, river authorities and manufacturers. Friendly persuasion was the order of the day, and it worked. Manufacturers voluntarily agreed to phase out 'hard' detergents in favour of biodegradable ones which could be broken down during sewage treatment. A very marked improvement to the Thames, and some other rivers, swiftly came on the heels of this application of co-operative common sense. As we read in the next chapter, this has been by no means industry's only contribution to the river.

Continuing guard is kept on the Thames: specialists watch over the river as doctors might do for an invalid who is convalescent but subject to possible relapse. At Beckton and Crossness outfalls samples are taken daily at high and low tide. From the Barrow Deep to Richmond samples are taken at twenty-nine points on a fortnightly cycle, by the launch *Thameswater*. The vessel is equipped for analyses that need to be made immediately: otherwise samples go to the laboratory at Crossness.

Thus is the health of the river constantly monitored: any minor ailment is at once corrected, continuing improvement joyously recorded.

The restoration of the tidal Thames is perhaps best demonstrated by the following simple table: Take the figure 900 as representing the general degree of pollution in 1950. Twenty-five years later it was 250. The confident projection is that in 1980 it will read 90 – a reduction of pollution over thirty years by a sensational 90 per cent.

Justifiably we can speak of 'the Thames saved'.

An Industrial Resolution

The industrial revolution brought new millions to London and placed an intolerable strain on already archaic sewerage. Factories added their vast quota of pollutants. All flowed into the Thames. At its worst, Charles Dickens graphically painted the picture in an issue of his journal *Household Words* in 1851. He penned an ironic dialogue with the river, which went, in part:

'But what is that floating by? – pah! it is a dead dog, or something . . . . How very thick the water is hereabouts, Father Thames; and, pray, may I inquire what that black, sluggish stream may be which I see pouring into you from a wide bricked archway, yonder?'

'Oh, that's one of my sewers,' replied the Father of Rivers . . . .

'But what are those smaller mouths that send forth strange party-coloured currents to mingle with your waters?'

'That one belongs to a soap-boiler – a particular friend of mine; the next to it is from a slaughter-house, kept by an estimable friend indeed, who wouldn't allow a particle of the refuse and drainage from his yards to run elsewhere, on any account . . . . Those other agreeable little outlets you are looking at, or will shortly see, on both sides of my banks, are from gas-works, brewhouses, shot-factories, coal-wharfs, cow-houses, tan-pits, gut-spinners, fish-markets and other cheerful and odiferous tributaries; while the inky flood yonder which your eyes are now fixed upon is from a very populous grave-yard, which produces so large a quantity of liquid every twenty-four hours, that it has to be drained off by regular arrangements, and made to flow into my convenient, all-embracing bosom.'

Dickens wonderfully summarized the near destruction of the Thames through uncontrolled industrial effluent. What a contrast with today. This book is much involved in contrasts – to the advantage of our own times. Generations to come should bless our foresight.

In the last year for which statistics are available as I write, only three prosecutions for pollution offences had to be initiated by the Thames Water Authority and one by the Port of London Authority. This illustrates an industrial *resolution* – an anti-pollution resolution – an appreciation by modern industries that whilst they may depend on the Thames, the Thames also depends on them. There is a widespread sentiment that control of pollution is a paramount responsibility of riverside factories. There is general regard for stringent regulations that most Victorians would have considered an outrageous interference. Above all, there is mutual respect between industry, Thames Water and P L A and a spirit of co-operation between the inspectorate and the commercial installations that line sectors of the Thames and its tributaries.

To emphasize this comparatively new attitude, and to give credit where it is due, I invited twelve major concerns to tell me, in lay language, of their effluent and pollution problems and how they solved them. I was gratified to receive answers from ten of them. Tate & Lyle Refineries Ltd, replied courteously saying that they do not have any significant effluent problems. The contributions of the Ford Motor Company to fish research I have referred to elsewhere. I should add that the industries mentioned here are intended simply as representative of the many more that collaborate to ensure a healthy Thames: others could claim, and merit, inclusion for their excellent activities.

An oil refinery

In the processing of crude oil at an older type oil refinery, a considerable quantity of water, as much as twenty tons for every ton of crude oil, can be used in the cooling of intermediate or finished products. Some of this cooling water inevitably becomes contaminated with oil, as does much of the rain water draining from the site, and therefore requires treatment before it can be discharged to the aqueous environment.

Shell Haven Refinery, from a river-side jetty. Situated on the north bank of the Thames mid-way between Tilbury and Southend, the refinery has a distilling capacity of 200 000 barrels a day. *Shell Photographic Library*

At the Shell Haven refinery of Shell U K Oil, the oil-contaminated water is passed through oil interceptors, which slow down the rate of flow and allow the oil to float to the surface. The oil is then removed and the clean water discharged to the Thames.

Over the last decade there have been considerable improvements to the operation and design of these interceptors. Reductions in the contamination at

source by better design, construction and mainten-ance of plant in general and oil coolers in particular, have resulted in a significant reduction in the contri-bution to the pollution load on the surroundings. New plants built within the last ten years make ex-tensive use of air cooling of oil which avoids many of the pollution problems already noted.

Water streams from refining processes can be heavily contaminated and they are purified and cleaned up in stripping units before going to drainage.

Another oil

Occupying a position on the banks of the Thames at Purfleet, Essex, is one of the largest food manufactu-rers in the country, Van den Berghs & Jurgens Ltd. Primarily concerned with the manufacture and sales of edible oils and fats, the company is very depend-ent on the river. It has its own deep-water berth, where tankers carrying crude edible oils from all parts of the world unload their cargoes.

Since 1918, the factory's only real environmental problem has been the large volumes of edible oil pro-cessing water used which have to be discharged – about ½ million gallons every day. The obvious way to dispose of this water was to pump it into the Thames after passing it through fat-traps, followed by simple clinker filters.

As long ago as 1950, shortly after the Port of London adopted a major clean-up campaign for the river, the Company, aware of its environmental res-ponsibilities, spent considerable time on developing a chemical effluent treatment plant. In the decade following 1960, the capital cost of making improve-ments to the effluent added up to about £¼ million. Labour, chemical and power costs added to the figure considerably.

But as production increased, so did effluent, and it was necessary to develop further plans so that effluent, rather than being discharged to the Thames, would be pumped to the local authority foul sewer.

Work was carried out on drainage improvements, re-designed fat-traps, a pipeline to the local authority sewer, and other detail changes in design to improve the cleanliness of the effluent.

Today, no trade effluent is being pumped to the Thames by Van den Burghs & Jurgens Ltd. To achieve this the Company has spent in excess of £½ million and is committed to heavy on-going costs. As the Company's Chief Engineer says, 'It has been a very time-consuming and costly exercise. However, we have always tried to discharge our social duties and will continue to support any measure to improve our environment.'

The paper industry

Legislation under the 1964 and 1968 Acts of Parliament gave the Port of London Authority necessary powers to require the polluting load of industrial discharges to the Tidal Thames to be reduced. In conjuction with the programme of reduction of domestic pollutants from GLC sewage treatment works in the Tidal Thames, discussions between the British Paper & Board Makers Association and the Port of London Authority's committee took place. An agreed programme of pollution reduction was drawn up between the six paper-making companies producing paper on the south bank of the Thames and was aimed at a reduction in the first instance of solids being discharged to the Thames.

Reed International Ltd say that the major problem in treating the effluent from a mill is that, by the very nature of its process, a mill uses very large quantities of water. Each mill effluent is of the order of several million gallons a day and contains up to 2000 milligrams of solids per litre in its discharge. Even so, in the production of paper a very high proportion of the water that is used is recycled and, from an economic point of view, each paper mill attempts to recover as much of the fibre and solids in its recycling as possible because of the high cost of the raw materials.

The first problem that the paper mills had to face in treating the volumes involved was the considerable space requirements for the treatment plant, for which large capital expenditure was required. Running costs of the plant are also high. In most cases this presented quite a severe problem as all the mills in question have been situated on their existing sites for at least sixty years and most available space had been used. Nevertheless, each company drew up its own plans for treatment and discussed these individually with the Port of London Authority.

Another problem for the individual manufacturers was the fact that the paper industry was not very well versed in effluent treatment and therefore had to carry out its own studies to find the most economic method of treatment. This has inevitably resulted in a diversity of plant being installed in different mills, because each paper mill's effluent is individual in character. The types of paper produced by the Thames-side mills vary considerably, including wrapping papers, tissues and high-quality coated printing papers, giving rise to each mill having quite a different effluent characteristic.

The installation of the treatment plants by the paper industry has succeeded in meeting the required standard of discharge, but has involved the industry in considerable capital expenditure. In addition, each mill had a very lengthy period of investigation involving considerable expense in manpower and technical expertise to achieve the final designs. During this period, some paper mills have closed, due to the severe recession that has taken place in the industry, and mills have suffered additional financial burdens at a difficult time.

The operation of the effluent plant has inevitably resulted in a further considerable problem, the disposal of the waste solids generated by the new settlement and filtration processes, usually to a disused quarry. Every day of operation requires removal of the solids from the effluent plant to a local tipping area, which, with rising oil prices, means considerable transport costs. Some difficulties have arisen because one or two of the wastes are toxic, and require special arrangements.

The industry has made a considerable and concerted effort to meet the Water Authority's requirements and, in general, very satisfactory results have been achieved in pollution reduction in the Thames.

There is no doubt that the British paper- and board-making industry is one of those industries in Britain which not only has a considerable influence on environmental standards, but also has taken up and is continuing to take up the challenge of meeting higher standards. At present the industry's water usage and effluent treatment is the main area of concern, and it is certainly a major problem considering that the industry is currently using about 287 million gallons of fresh water per day for process and cooling purposes, which makes it one of the largest water-using industries in the country.

A particular case

One of the most novel and highly successful anti-pollution approaches adopted by a British company has been the installation of river aerators by Thames Board Mills Ltd at its Purfleet Mill, which with a capacity approaching 300 000 tonnes of board each year makes it probably the world's largest paperboard mill. The volume of process water discharged into the Thames from the mill amounts to approximately 5 million gallons per day. This takes a large quantity of oxygen from the river. Further to refine the pollution prevention measures with a land based filtration unit was recognized to be extremely expensive and further complicated by the very limited land area available on the Purfleet site for the treatment of effluent. Conventional effluent treatment would in effect mean pumping the effluent to a treatment site nearly two miles away from the mill and subsequently pumping it back, thus adding very heavily to costs.

The approach to the effluent problem finally adopted represented an entirely new technique in tidal waters, and involved building and launching surface aerators, which pump oxygen back into the river so as to compensate directly for the oxygen demand of the mill's effluent. River aeration on this scale had never before been attempted in tidal waters in any part of the world, and the scheme was conceived and developed, and has been successfully installed by the Technical Division of the Company. Five years of investigation and planning was needed before the first aerator could be launched in 1971.

It was essential to have the largest possible interfacial area between the air and water so as to allow the oxygen to diffuse from the air into the water most efficiently.

It was also necessary to prevent local build-up of oxygen concentrates by promoting good mixing within the water. It had to be borne in mind that only 8 lb. of oxygen could be dissolved in every million pounds of water before the river reached its oxygen saturation point. It was therefore vital that the water near the aerator was constantly changing.

The result of feasibility tests led to Thames Board commissioning the construction of a 200-horsepower aerator by Ames Crosta, the largest known single unit ever manufactured. The aerator was put into operation in the Thames off Erith, about two miles from Thames's Purfleet Mills, at a point where aeration would have most effect on the condition of the river. A second unit of similar design, but powered with a 300-horsepower motor was next installed. The two units together fully compensate for the existing effluent load on the river resulting from Thames's board-making operation.

Surface aeration on a large scale has successfully provided an answer to the effluent problem at Thames's Purfleet Mill.

Electricity comes clean

The Central Electricity Generating Board has a statutory duty to operate its plant with a proper concern for the environment. In many respects, its research leads the world in scientific knowledge of the behaviour of potential pollutants and their control.

As far as the Thames is concerned, there are two ways in which the Board's activities can – theoretically – contribute to its pollution: by raising the temperature of the water and by discharging chemicals into the water. Power stations need huge volumes of water for cooling purposes. Cold water passes through a station and is discharged at an inevitably higher temperature. Since rises in temperature impair oxygenation of water, fears have been expressed about this thermal pollution. However, in the immediate vicinity of a power station, increase in water temperature is rarely greater than 10°C. Moderate heating of water has no effect on oxygen content unless the water is nearly saturated with it. In such cases, a small reduction in oxygen is not important to biological life.

The greatest volume of warmed water is discharged when power stations are running flat out. As most stations on the Thames are required to run at maximum capacity only on the coldest winter days, slightly raised temperatures in these circumstances are of little consequence.

The biggest power stations on the Thames – which run for longer periods – are situated well downstream where the larger volumes of cold tidal water further reduce water temperatures generally.

In order to control atmospheric pollution, the CEGB 'washes' most of the sulphur dioxide from the flue gases of its Bankside power station. As a result of this process, very small quantities of lime and carbon dioxide enter the Thames. However, taking the year as a whole when, for the most part, the situation is running well below maximum

The Thames Board Mills' floating aerator

capacity, the overall effect is barely measurable.

All CEGB stations use oil traps to ensure that no waste oil – either for fuelling the station or for lubrication – is allowed to get into the Thames. When work is completed on the Thames Barrier, the effect of power station operations is expected to have little or no impact on Thames pollution under normal flood control conditions. In a full-scale emergency it might be necessary – for technical reasons – to run stations at well below maximum power in order to limit the temperature rise which might otherwise occur.

Ancient yet modern

Garton Sons & Company is a long-established riverside company producing glucose syrups, starch, and animal feedstuffs, and still uses some old buildings and manufacturing plant. This company is a large user of the Thames for the transport of several thousand tons of raw materials each year,

Power stations in the Tideway catch enormous quantities of fish in their intake screens

and also as a source of vast quantities of cooling water every day. Each of these activities can lead to pollution of the Tideway, but over the years there has been a continuous improvement in the situation.

Pollution caused by spillages during the off-loading of raw materials from barges has now been all but eliminated by the use of modern maize unloading facilities.

The collapse of the old culverts returning used cooling water to the Tideway, and old road drains along the wharfside formerly discharging to the Thames, have caused problems from time to time. These are being dealt with, however, and all road drains have already been diverted to the main sewage system; only the main culvert outfall is now used to return cooling water to the river. The company are continuing with work replacing flooring levels within the old plant to divert any spillages well clear of culvert runs to the main sewer system.

The biggest step forward will be around the year 1978, when the company's new refinery is due to come on stream, and the old glucose plant will be redundant. The new plant will use indirect cooling (i.e. surface condensers) and a cooling tower system. It is now accepted company policy that all new evaporation equipment will be cooled in this manner.

This in time will almost eliminate the use of river water as a coolant, and thereby remove all chance of pollution.

Soap and detergents

Procter & Gamble Ltd, manufacturer of soaps and detergents, has for long recognized that it has an obligation to safeguard the environment at its factories, one of which is on the Thames at West Thurrock.

At West Thurrock the company has contributed to the cleaning up of the Thames by making sure that waste discharges to the river meet or are ahead of the quality standards required by the Thames Water Authority, with whom it works in close consultation.

The approach to controlling liquid wastes is simple and straightforward. Here are some examples of techniques used: to prevent the risk of accidental spills from tanks and tank cars draining into the Thames, low containing walls around the tank fields have been built; in some cases effluents have been eliminated by converting them into saleable materials; wherever possible process wastes are recycled or re-used; remaining wastes are treated to make them acceptable in quantity and quality to the Authority before discharge to the town sewer; in a few cases it is necessary to use specialist waste disposal contractors to remove liquid waste for further treatment.

While sophisticated control equipment is important, success can only come from its correct operation by people committed to environmental protection and trained in their responsibilities.

At Proctor & Gamble's factory is a pollution control officer whose duties include the continuous monitoring of all discharges from the site. But, more importantly, *everyone* at the factory is trained to take responsibility for proper waste disposal and to draw attention to any problem which he or she cannot deal with personally.

Sugar keeps Thames sweet

The basic process carried out by the Albion Sugar Company Ltd, Woolwich, consists of grinding maize and extracting, by liquid separation techniques, the starch and protein fractions. The starch is then converted into glucose syrup. The protein is dried and mixed with the dried fibre residue from the maize to make cattle food.

The liquid separation part of the process when running normally is a closed circuit. That is, most of the aqueous phase is recycled and used again as process water so that there is no drain discharge. One part of this process is concerned with evaporating a 6 per cent protein solution to 50 per cent solids, and a spray condenser was used to cool the exhaust vapours. This highly polluting condensate was discharged into the river. The condenser was replaced about two years ago by an indirect condenser and the cooling water going to the river was pure. More recently even this has been stopped and it now goes back to a cooling tower, thus eliminating discharge.

In the part of the plant where glucose is made, one part of the process deals with the concentration by evaporation of glucose, under vacuum. Naturally there is a danger of solids being drawn into the vacuum system and discharged. This discharge used to be to the river, and later to the main drain from the site. However, it has now also been diverted back to the cooling tower.

That's the spirit

At Wandsworth, a very large distillery is operated by John Watney & Co, a centuries-old Thames-side firm and subsidiary of The Distillers Company. Its contribution to the fight against river pollution won it, in 1975, one of the two first silver medals (for single plants) awarded by The Angling Foundation and presented by Lord Nugent, Chairman of the National Water Council. (At the same time the Foundation's first gold medal went to John Watney's parent company for its work in preventing pollution from whisky distilleries in Scotland.) John Watney's produce huge quantities of grain spirit (potable ethyl alcohol) and carbon dioxide. Effluents are now discharged to Thames Water Authority sewers. Not for years has Watney's put effluent directly into the Thames from its plant. As in the case of Distillers in Scotland, Watney's use their treated effluent, 'spent wash' (the liquor remaining after distillation), to mix with cereal residues to produce animal feed: conservationists laud this as double benefit.

I trust I have not intruded too many technicalities into this chapter. At a time when it is popular to decry industry, I deem it right to bring to the attention of the general reader the significant contributions made by various industrial plants, at considerable cost, to a purer tidal Thames.

4 ALL CREATURES GREAT AND SMALL

Return of the Fishes

*This noble river, the Thames, yields an infinite plenty
of excellent sweet, and pleasant fish . . . . What should
I say of the fat and sweet Salmon daily taken in this
stream, and in such plenty after the time for Smelt is
passed that no river in Europe is able to exceed it?*

RAPHAEL HOLINSHEAD (died *c.* 1580),
Chronicles (modernized)

One hundred species?

At the commencement of the reign of Queen Elizabeth II, except for unusual incidents and lowly forms
– and some robust and ubiquitous Eels – fish life
was virtually extinct in the tidal Thames, that Royal
River from whose waters Queen Elizabeth I enjoyed
many succulent feasts. A return to such piscine
bounty is still in the future but since 1964, when the
very first effects of the modern anti-pollution programme became apparent, ninety-one species of fish
(plus one hybrid) have been found in the Tideway.
The ambition of biologists – who are capable of
such emotion – to discover one hundred species of
fish by the end of Jubilee Year is thus within sight.
In fact, if *all* forms of marine life were listed –
including the occasional seal – the figure could now

be claimed. I have heard of plans to try to reintroduce native oysters in Stangage Creek: shades of past Roman gourmets!

The latest addition to such a full list to come to my notice was the re-appearance of a creature so strange that I feel it deserves some space. The animal in question is the Chinese Mitten Crab whose claws are covered with thick fur – unusual in aquatic life. A marine biologist with whom I discussed this phenomenon was unable to say why this mitten exists: certainly not to keep the crab's claws warm! It may be that by apparently enlarging the weapons it makes more effective their deterrent menace to predators. The Mitten Crab is equally at home off the coast of China's Fukien province and in Korean ricefields and rivers – or English waters! A male specimen was found at Chelsea in 1935 – and another turned up in a Yorkshire reservoir in 1949. The three of these hardy crustaceans discovered in

Enigma from the East a Chinese Mitten Crab found in the Thames in 1976

1976 probably arrived in larval state in ship's ballast: if they can establish themselves they will provide an exotic oriental addition to the Thames. Less likely to do so is that popular marine oddity the Sea Horse: one was found at Dagenham in 1976, probably the only one ever taken from British waters other than the English Channel.

Though perhaps more dramatic than practical, these two isolated discoveries do show how the tidal Thames is now able to support varied marine life to an extent that would have seemed unlikely a decade ago – and was a pipe-dream a quarter of a century ago.

Since the public evinces a continual interest in any reference to Thames Salmon – although this attention may exaggerate the actual importance of the topic – I propose to deal separately with the possible re-introduction of that species. There have been, and are, more practical fish to fry.

More typical than Salmon of the Thames commercial fishing of yester-year was the Whitebait industry. Whitebait are immature herring and sprats (and some other species) in their first year. In the late eighteenth and early nineteenth centuries, Whitebait were landed in vast quantities around Greenwich and Blackwall. They were not only a seasonal delight in local pubs but were a delicacy at the royal court, and featured in civic gastronomy – which often dissolved into gluttony. By the mid-nineteenth century, pollution had killed the river fisheries and the Whitebait industry migrated down the estuary to the Southend area.

A relation of the Salmon, the Smelt, was also a major Thames fish. It is mis-named, for its odour, akin to cucumber, is delicious: it fries to perfection. A writer, around 1835, recorded: 'Formerly, the Thames from Wandsworth to Putney Bridge, and from thence upwards to Hammersmith, produced abundance of Smelts, and from thirty to forty boats might be seen working together: but very few are now taken, the state of the water, it is believed, preventing the fish advancing so high up.'

Lamperns (river Lamprey) – primitive parasites much relished by gourmets – Eels and Flounders were commomly harvested in the tidal Thames. Gravesend was noted for its shrimps. All these activities succumbed to the dying river or were driven downstream: the freshwater fish retired to the comparatively clean upper reaches. An early seventeenth-century pictorial map of central London's riverside gives prominence to 'eell schipes'. These brought live Eels to Billingsgate from Holland, but this traffic, too, ceased as even Eels eventually were killed by the fouled Thames water in which they were stored live prior to sale.

Mr Alwyne Wheeler, the marine biologist, to whose researches I am much indebted, has pointed out that there was a temporary – I repeat, temporary – revival of fish in the Thames, after chemical treatment of sewage began at the principal outfalls at the end of the last century. By 1895 Whitebait were again caught at Greenwich; Smelt were taken as far upstream as Teddington. Roach, Dace and other fish

Sea Horse found at Dagenham in 1976

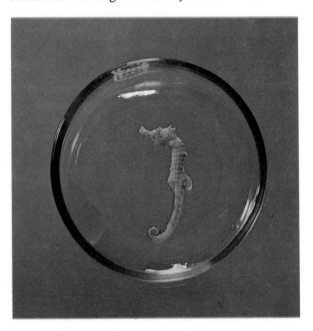

which had retreated to the non-tidal river appeared downstream at Putney, and by 1900 were caught at Westminster. Roach got as far as Woolwich.

But in the inter-war years the tidal Thames was again neglected and it deteriorated. There was a lack of research, and surprisingly little interest shown in the condition of the lower Thames in general. It is believed that by 1932 no sea fish wished to penetrate higher than Gravesend. Of euryhaline fish – which tolerate (or seasonally demand) fresh water and brackish or sea water – Eels alone probably survived. A peculiar circumstance was the discovery of large Stickleback colonies in emergency water tanks installed at Chelsea in the Second World War: these were filled directly from the river, which was thought to contain no fish at that point.

A survey in 1957 indicated that below Richmond there were no significant aquatic organisms in the Thames whilst it flowed through London: one needed to go well below the Port of London before encountering any substantial fish life in the river.

The Port of London Act of 1964 implemented the 1961 report of 'Pollution of the Tidal Thames', published under the chairmanship of Prof. A.J.C. Pippard. This report resulted from a series of meetings, initiated in 1951, at which the government consulted on the question of the Thames with all the diverse bodies then concerned – Thames Conservancy, Port of London, London County Council, Metropolitan Water Board, riverine industry, specialist groups and individuals, Borough Councils, and so on. Broadly, Prof. Pippard's Committee recommended that measures be taken to render the tidal Thames 'inoffensive', to ensure a dissolved oxygen content in the whole river of not less than 10 per cent – it was then nil in places – and eventually to make the river suitable for Salmon. The last criterion was established less with any serious notion to turn the Thames into a Salmon river than because a river capable of supporting Salmon would need to be a very clean river. How these objectives were attained

I have outlined in a previous chapter: it is the effect on fish with which we are here concerned.

From 1965, when fish were found at Fulham electricity station, the Central Electricity Generating Board arranged to collect and preserve fish found in the screens which intercept debris in water drawn from the Thames for cooling purposes at their riverside installations. This co-operation has proved scientifically of great value, as four important sections of the Tideway are now covered – Fulham, Blackwall, Barking and West Thurrock, near the Dartford Tunnel. Sampling has been on a regular basis since 1967. In recent years, 'catches' at power stations have sometimes proved almost embarrassingly heavy! Dead fish are kept for statistics and a proportion for scientific analysis. Live ones are designated and eventually returned to the river, in the hope they may have learned a lesson and stay away from intakes in future. Other industries employing river water also keep a sporadic watch for unusual fish: Ford's generating plant at Dagenham has provided interesting specimens.

In the Dartford Tunnel sector, Flounders are now very common, and Whiting, Dab, Plaice, Sole and Brill are plentiful. In winter, Herring and Sprats are found in large quantities. Extracts from some recent samplings show the variety and quantity of fish now thriving in the Tideway. In four hours, from three screens, at West Thurrock: 2564 Whiting, 60 Sprat, 34 Flounders, 10 Dab, 9 Eel, 9 Bass, 9 Codling, 7 Herring, 5 Sole, 2 Plaice, a large number of less familiar fish – and a single anchovy. On another day, in six hours, from five screens a haul of 3117 Whiting was made, plus many other varieties. From two screens at Ford's in rather over an hour one morning, 103 Sprat were taken, and, amongst other miscellaneous fish, that unique Sea Horse. As commercial fishing on any scale does not occur above Southend – and trawling would be impracticable on the reaches in question – these fortuitous industrial catches are of great value in indicating the gratifying extent of the 'return of the fishes'. Thames Water also has its own craft to garner specimens. Grey Mullet and Bass are other well-known fish increasingly found, as well as the popular Haddock, which Mr Wheeler finds of special interest since the breed was almost unknown in the southern North Sea before 1966. He surmises that a surge in the Scottish Haddock population in 1963 caused a southwards migration in search of food. Haddock have been found as far upstream as Barking. Conversely, freshwater fish have penetrated downstream to the same reaches – notably Roach, Carp, and one errant Pike. Smelt, a migrant species, have found their way upstream as far as Fulham and this is taken as a particularly good indication of the salubrious state of the river: they come from the sea and can evidently survive the remaining somewhat polluted areas. The old London docks, decaying in favour of Tilbury, are providing a prolific fish source: mussels abound – though their consumption is not yet recommended.

This is not a book in which to list fully the fish of the Thames; I am concerned with the broad picture. It is one that changes with the seasons. Particularly at Barking, traditionally the most contaminated part of the river, catches in winter are far better than in summer, when the fresh water flow into the river is lower and oxygen content decreases. But long-term alterations at Beckton sewage treatment works have improved the quality of the effluent it discharges at Barking and the fish will benefit.

The summer of 1976 provided a severe test. Flow over Teddington Weir was for months negligible, tributaries dwindled; the natural accretion of fresh water to the lower Thames declined and the salinity increased. However, it is a tribute to the great improvement in effluent entering the river that few ill effects occurred. The stream remained healthy, shrimps swarmed at Hammersmith; the fish survived happily.

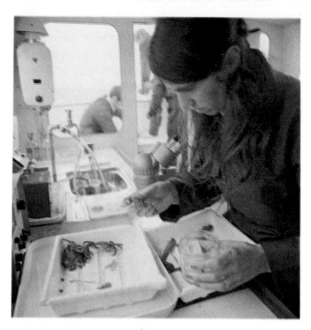

Sorting the catch aboard the Authority's floating laboratory, *Thames-water*

Fish mean angling, and angling is Britain's most popular single outdoor recreation, so it is pleasant to see patient men, rod in hand, on reaches where such an occupation would have been entirely futile – even unpleasant – only a few years ago.

On the freshwater river, angling has always been worthwhile, and, despite my proper preoccupation with the tidal section, I should perhaps refer briefly to piscatorial developments on the upper reaches and ancillary waters. There are successful trout fisheries in reservoirs at Walthamstow and Kempton Park in London, and at Wroughton, near Swindon. The fishery potential of reservoirs under construction at Datchet, Berkshire, and Farmoor, Oxfordshire, has been assessed and at Datchet a trout fishery was opened in 1976. At Barn Elms Reservoir, Hammersmith, an experimental period of trout fishing – using any bait bar grubs – has proved popular: best results come by spinning or fly casting. In areas under Thames Water Authority control, lakes, pits and, above all, tributary rivers –

Patience rewarded.
A happy angler on
the foreshore
opposite the Tate
Gallery

are capable of considerable development and improvement from a fish, thus an angling, viewpoint. Fisheries maintenance and development is largely financed by rod-licences, the fees for which are very reasonable (in view of inflation I give no prices), minimal for old age pensioners and the disabled, and the traditional right of youngsters – under sixteen – to fish free has been upheld.

To revert to our main subject, and to quote the dedicated Mr Alwyne Wheeler (writing in *Science Journal*):

The recovery of the lower Thames has been an encouraging development from the improvements made in sewage treatment in the London area. The re-establishment of its fish fauna soon after completion of work at Crossness [and now at Beckton] shows what adaptable animals fishes really are. Indeed, it took them only seven years to re-populate a habitat from which they had been excluded for many decades. The future outlook is hopeful . . . .

The lower Thames should be reinforced in its position as an example to the world of the benefits of pollution control. To have a cleaner river is an improvement. But to have fish living in the river is a major advance. As many pollution control officers have discovered, the presence of a percentage of dissolved oxygen in the water is a nebulous concept – being invisible, odourless and tasteless – but a live fish taken out of the same water is a measure of the health of a river which everybody can understand and appreciate.

The fish of the Thames – whether in copious supply or as a unique specimen, edible or curious – now read as a proud piscatory roll-call: Barbel, Bass, Bleak, Bream and Bullhead . . . Carp, Chub and Conger . . . Dory and Dragonet . . . Goldfish and Gudgeon . . . Herring and Hooknose . . . Loach and Lumpsucker . . . tasty Mackeral, humble Minnow, voracious Pike and placid Plaice . . . Rudd and Ruffe . . . Sand Goby, Scad and succulent Sea Trout . . . Skipper and Sprat . . . Tench, Twaite Shad, Whiting . . . Sea Horse, of course . . . and Salmon?

Again a Salmon river?

Whether the Thames can ever again become a Salmon river – whether, indeed, it is desirable or practicable that it should – is polemical. That, in theory, it could be so is not in doubt. The average dissolved oxygen level of around 30 per cent is certainly tolerable to the existence and spawning of this prized game fish.

Mr D. J. Solomon, whom I was delighted to see gives the Thames the title of England's longest river, contributed an authoritative survey of the topic to the *London Naturalist* in 1975 and I acknowledge a debt to his erudition. The Thames once supported a large population of migratory fish, of which the Salmon was the most prestigious if not the most commercially important. Yet in 1766 one hundred and thirty Thames Salmon were sold in one day at Billingsgate. Mr Solomon rightly opines that pollution was not wholly responsible for the retreat, and final withdrawal, of Salmon from the Thames. Over-fishing, and engineering – docks, locks, artificial weirs – also played their part. Not that upper Thames catches were, since records were kept, very considerable: most fish were trapped lower down. However, over sixty Salmon were taken at Boulters Weir, Maidenhead, in 1801 and again in 1804. At the same spot none was captured in 1820 and only two the next year. At Windsor in 1820 a twenty-pounder was caught and sold to the Royal Court for the then huge sum of £1 per pound, indicating its scarcity. In 1821, £1.50 a pound was offered for a Thames Salmon to serve at George IV's Coronation banquet: none was caught in time. Too late, a couple were landed in the lower reaches a day after the event.

It is conceded that the last Salmon caught upstream from London was in 1833. Occasional individual kills and sightings continued to be reported up to 1862 in the lower Thames. In 1863 a five-pounder was reported in the Darent, a lower tributary, and in the next year a quantity of young Salmon were released into the Thames from a hatchery on the Lee. Other similar experiments took place. These confused the true position, because Salmon were again taken from time to time, but efforts to re-stock the river were nullified by the increasing pollution with which we are now only too well aquainted.

Migratory fish, especially the fastidious Salmon, definitely could not survive in water so filthy that it killed human beings, as was tragically illustrated in September 1878. The Thames pleasure steamer *Princess Alice* sank after a collision in the vicinity of Barking, a stretch notoriously polluted – not only by sewage but by highly toxic effluent from what was then Europe's largest gas works. (A scientist found that effluent from this plant killed an Eel in five minutes.) Of 640 people lost in the disaster, a number

Some fish found in the tidal Thames. These are listed in descending order; *left:* Bleak, Crucian Carp, Chub; *centre:* Whiting, Codling, Bass, Minnows; *right:* Bib, Bream, Pike

were known to be good swimmers. The horrible state of the bodies recovered suggested to doctors that they had perished from poisoning and suffocation in the fetid depths rather than by drowning. What chance had a Salmon – any fish for that matter – of passing such a fatal reach? A dark perod, with a brief respite already referred to, settled on the Thames.

The finding of Sea Trout, a fairly close relative of the Salmon, in 1971, at Deptford and Teddington, gave rise for optimism about the possible return of important migratory fish. Two years later, the Port of London Authority considered the possibility of Salmon sufficiently well-founded to offer an annual prize of £500 for the largest Salmon taken by rod and line between Teddington and Southend. Sanguine expectations were not realized: in anticipation of this it had been announced that in the event of no Salmon being caught, the prize would go to the captor of the largest Sea Trout. No one claimed it. A twenty-eight pound Salmon was found dead in the Medway – the major estuarine tributary, now more polluted than the Thames – and a smaller one was brought out alive from near the same spot by the river authority. No one qualifying for the main prize, a smaller one was given for a Sea Trout caught just seawards of the designated area.

Considerable excitement followed the discovery of a Salmon, which did not long survive the experience, drawn into an intake screen at West Thurrock in November 1974. This followed very heavy rain. But such events, which may again occur, are freakish: Hampshire and Yorkshire have the closest Salmon rivers to the Thames and for a homing Salmon to make for the Thames, it must be sick or badly disorientated.

As to the future, it is a declared policy of the Thames Water Authority fully to investigate the 'feasibility of introducing Salmon to the River Thames'. The Authority's last annual report stated, 'Salmon fry have been placed in three tributaries of the river to monitor their growth, dispersion and survival. . . . The authority will need to give detailed consideration to the practical and economic implications of restoring a migratory fish population to the River Thames.'

It is not an easy matter. Migratory fish can, at the right time, pass upstream through Teddington Weir without difficulty, but at present they could hardly pass Molesey. To allow Salmon to get to the upper reaches, which alone in the main stream present adequate spawning grounds, would require the building of costly fish ladders – at the moment of writing, at least, unlikely to prove a popular way to spend public funds. So tributaries seem the most promising areas. The Darent provides 'excellent conditions for spawning' in the estimation of Jeffery Harrison and Peter Grant (*The Thames Trans-*

formed). No engineering work would be involved.

However, other factors must be considered. By no means would all anglers welcome the intrusion of game fish into their coarse fish waters. Successful raising of Salmon would also greatly raise the value of fishing rights, and riparian ownership is varied and complicated. Would the present, somewhat precarious, ecology be upset, with new species fighting for a by no means inexhaustible food supply?

We do not know how the Salmon fry will fare; whether the oxygen supply really is consistently sufficient; whether the tiny Salmon can survive disease and escape predators in satisfactory numbers. There are too any imponderables for a final answer to be given for years to come.

Most Londoners would like to see the Thames a Salmon river. The will to make it so certainly exists, the same will which ensured that the river is again a fit home for a multitude of other fish.

Truly, Father Thames lives.

The Birds Fly Back

Sweet Swan of Avon! what a sight it were
To see thee in our waters yet appear,
And make those flights upon the banks of Thames,
That so did take Eliza, and our James.

BEN JOHNSON (1573-1637), *To the Memory of My Be-*
loved, the Author, Mr William Shakespeare

The British love of angling, now being so well catered for on the Thames, is rivalled by their adoration of dogs. Regrettably, the only canine association with the river is the Isle of Dogs. This was so called because Charles II, who liked to reside at Greenwich, had the palace pets sent across the river at night so that their barking – which is *not* the origin of the neighbouring borough of that name – might not disturb his slumber. He was, of course, himself a dog-lover: has any other Sovereign had a breed named for him?

However, if I cannot say more about dogs, I can indeed indulge another British passion – for birds.

The success of anti-pollution measures has had a remarkable effect on bird life on the inner tidal Thames. Obviously, the return of fish has encouraged the re-appearance of fish-eating birds, and many others have found the cleansed environment suits them.

According to a report on 'The Conservation of Birdlife on the Inner Thames', by Mr E. J. Grant (Editor, *London Bird Report* 1969-71) and Mr J. G. Harrison (Chairman, Wildfowl Conservation Committee, Nature Conservancy), the increase in wildfowl and waders wintering on the Thames commenced in the early 1960s. Now large flocks are to be seen, particularly in the reaches from Silvertown to Tilbury whence they had for years been driven by the previous poor conditions: less foul, more fowl! The report's conclusions:

With the total population now regularly exceeding 10 000, the area is classed in the top category of sites of *international* importance to wildfowl conservation.

These flocks bring spectacular natural beauty, life and colour to London's grey riverside scenery. The creation of a prime new bird habitat so close to London in what seemed a hopeless situation is a remarkable achievement, and a splended example which may hopefully be followed in other polluted rivers and waters of the world. The presence of these birds is a constant visible proof that all is well with the natural environment of the river.

The following references from the report to the most important wildfowl areas may be mainly of interest to the ornithologically-minded: they indicate promising locations for bird-watchers. But they also show the extent of returning birdlife and outline conservation problems that lie ahead.

Low-tide mud between Woolwich Ferry and Margaret Ness. First used by large numbers of duck during 1970-71 winter. but numbers increasing annually with up to 600 Pochard and 610 Mallard.

Low-tide mud between Margaret Ness and Crossness. By far the most important site along the inner Thames, but unfortunately already seriously threatened by plans to extend the river embankment out over the mud as part of the Thamesmead development. These plans were finalized before 1968-9 when duck first began feeding here in large numbers however, but illustrates the sort of development which should be avoided if wildlife is to be preserved along the river. The effect of extending the embankment will almost certainly be catastrophic. In recent years up to 700 Mallard, 700 Teal, 330 Pintail, 800 Tufted Duck, 4000 Pochard, 1600 Shelduck and 2000 Dunlin have been counted in this bay.

Low-tide mud in the bay to the east of Barking Power Station. A very important site, probably crucially so in view of the impending destruction of the Woolwich bay site on the opposite side of the river, for which it may provide an alternative feeding area. Up to 326 Mallard, 630 Teal, 95 Pintail, 100 Tufted Duck, 1500 Pochard, 800 Shelduck, 30 Dunlin and 5 Redshank have been seen at this site. Open ground bordering this bay would be an ideal area for future conservation into parkland.

Low-tide mud at mouth of Barking creek. A relatively small area which attracts a surprisingly large population of Mallard, Shelduck and Lapwing.

Low-tide mud which surrounds the Swanscombe 'headland' from Greenhithe to Northfleet. A most important area, most of which must be preserved if the large and varied bird population is to be retained. Up to 30 Mallard, 100 Teal, 160 Wigeon, 20 Pintail, 700 Pochard, 1500 Shelduck, 1000 Lapwing, 30 Ringed Plover, 420 Redshank, 90 Ruff and 3500 Dunlin have been seen in recent years. Open ground which makes up most of the headland is of major importance to wildlife.

Low-tide mud from Stone Ness to Purfleet. Although this heavily industrialized stretch of the river is too disturbed and built up to attract large numbers of wildfowl,

Swans at Bow Creek; here the tidal flood-prevention barrier lies across the River Lee where it joins the Thames

Heron catching an Eel While Herons feed in small numbers on the foreshore of the tidal Thames, most frequent the riverside marshes. *By courtesy of the Royal Society for the Protection of Birds; photo: Michael W. Richards*

waders appear to be more tolerant and this area is perhaps the most important one on the river for this group of birds. Perhaps most interesting among this wader population are the Ruff, rare birds in the London area as a whole but up to 130 are seen regularly, as well as vast flocks of Dunlin (up to 3000) and up to 300 Redshank. Up to 880 Shelduck, 55 Pintail and 75 Mallard have been seen but such high numbers of duck are rather exceptional in this area.

A quiet inlet at Silvertown, surrounded by open ground resulting from demolition attracted up to 35 Pochard during the 1971-2 winter and during the 1972-3 winter numbers had increased with up to 465 Pochard, 69 Tufted Duck and 72 Mallard. This site is the furthest point upriver recorded for large numbers of duck so far.

A grain wharf near the entrance of Bow Creek attracts a flock of up to 345 Mute Swans which feed on spillages.

Low-tide mudflats between Crossness and Belvedere Power Station. An important area for wildfowl and waders, which will form a crucial replacement feeding area for birds which may be displaced by the destruction of the mudflats in the Woolwich bay. Recent counts include up to 400 Mallard, 101 Pintail, 468 Pochards, 154 Shelduck, 70 Mute Swans and 1100 Dunlin.

Low-tide mudflats between Coldharbour Point and Purfleet. In recent winters up to 200 Mallard, 54 Wigeon, 26 Pintail, 600 Pochard, 850 Shelduck, 12 Ringed Plovers, 95 Snipe, 70 Redshank. Open ground backing on to this area is of major importance to wildlife.

Low-tide mud from Erith to Greenhithe and the River Darent estuary. This site is of major importance to waders. Up to 5000 Dunlin, 450 Lapwing, 250 Redshank, 75 Ruff and 700 Shelduck have been seen in recent winters. Open ground at present borders most of this section and this should be preserved.

Low-tide mud between Stone Ness and Grays. Quite an important area. Recent counts include up to 60 Mallard, 90 Shelduck, 1000 Dunlin, 463 Redshank, and 30 Ringed Plover.

Riverside Open Land

An area of rough derelict land extending approximately ½ mile to the east of Barking Power Station, and the riverside footpath from this area eastwards along the river wall. An ideal area for future conversion into a public open space. Landscaped and planted with trees, this area could be transformed into an extremely pleasant open space and riverside walk. Developed in this way it would provide the necessary seclusion required by the birdlife which at present is found in the area.

The area of Thamesmead. As already stated, the plans for extending the river embankment over the mudflats in the Woolwich bay is regrettable. Plans to have riverside open spaces in this area are welcomed however, and this should benefit the bird population at Woolwich Ferry.

Rainham 'marshes'. The sludge lagoons in this area are an important bird habitat in their own right. Attractive riverside walks/parkland could be created from the factory area in the north-west of this land to the outlet of the Mar Dyke at the eastern end. Special conservation of certain riverside grass habitats and reed beds in the area would maintain their attraction for particularly rare bird species which inhabit them at present.

Swanscombe Marshes. A fascinating area for wildlife in general, containing many unique habitats for the London area. Several sections would be ideally suitable for management as permanent nature reserves, and would add greatly to the environment of any future residential developments which may be planned for the area.

I shall go into no more details on the birds of the inner tidal Thames. I refer interested persons to the extremely comprehensive survey by Mr Jeffery Harrison and Peter Grant in their *The Thames Transformed* (see Chapter 6). The authors rightly claim that the story of the devastation of the inner Thames and its restoration – and the return of fish and waterfowl – had not been fully recounted previously 'simply because such an astonishing thing has never been achieved before. This is something in which Britain leads the world.'

Whilst a little worried by the loss of wildfowl feeding grounds through the raising of flood defence walls down river from the Barrier, Mr Harrison and Mr Grant are more alarmed about the marshlands of the Outer Thames, the estuary, and of the big tributary to it, the Medway – which attracts hosts of migratory geese. If effected, a proposal for new docks in the Medway estuary – instead of, or in addition to, the Maplin Sands projects – they consider would be devastating.

They make a very logical – not the least cranky – conservationist case. They do not oppose development, only development wrongly sited.

So the wildfowl have come back. Tribute to this was paid when the Fifth International Conference on the Conservation of Wetlands and Waterfowl (1974) sent special congratulations from thirty-five nations to the P L A and G L C, whose main conservational work is now in the hands of the Thames Water Authority.

Yet it must be reiterated that the Inner Thames success should be viewed against the dangers to the more varied and numerous wildfowl of the lower estuary. These are clouds there: let us hope public awareness and political sense will not allow them to bring a storm.

5 THE WAY AHEAD

The silver Thames, her own domestic flood,
Shall bear her vessels like a sweeping train,
And often wind, as of his mistress proud,
With longing eyes to meet her face again.

JOHN DRYDEN (1631-1700), after the Great Fire of
London

Thames Water, with responsibilities for 'its vast
urban population and significant re-use of water,
must be at the forefront of knowledge regarding
water-borne diseases and the polluting by-products
of modern technology', to quote the recent annual
report of the Authority. It is the abolition of pollution which is my primary subject, yet in projecting
into the future other considerations must be taken
into account. One development in particular has
relevance.

It would be no good making the tidal Thames
splendidly salubrious if these waters were to be in-
adequately controlled. Floods are a form of pollution. I can remember when in 1928 the Thames
overflowed at Millbank (north side) and Lambeth
(south) and fourteen were drowned. Writing in Jubilee Year, it is sad to recall that it was in Coronation
Year, 1953, that devastating floods swept the East
Coast and the Thames estuary killing 300.

Not that Thames floods are anything new. Within
living memory, almost annual flooding around
Maidenhead was an accepted hazard of life. Flooding is a seasonal nuisance around Barnes, Putney
and Chiswick: it has always been thus and the riverside housing has long been planned accordingly. In
fact such safe flooding is beneficial in relieving
pressure elsewhere – an aqueous safety valve.

But should some historic inundations of central
London itself be repeated in modern conditions, the

results would be horrifying. On a December day in 1663, Pepys recorded in his diary: 'There was last night the greatest tide that was ever remembered in England to have been in this river, all Whitehall having been drowned'. The Thames was not then, of course, fully embanked as it flowed through the capital and some flooding was expected, if not as serious as it had been in 1236 when men rowed boats inside Westminster Hall, built on reclaimed marshland.

Immediate dangers on the estuary have been greatly decreased by interim measures, mainly the raising of banks. Yet these potentially increase the hazard to London, by forcing extra water upstream. South-east England is sinking at the geologically alarming rate of a foot a century, and London is sinking on its own bed of clay. Tide levels have risen over the past hundred years by one foot at Southend and by twice that at London Bridge. The Thames is also subject to surge tides – meteorological phenomena whose scientific explanation has no place here. If this extra mass of water joins a normal high tide, the threat of flooding becomes serious: it was such tidal conjunction, abetted by wind, that caused the 1953 floods. Twenty-four square miles are severely endangered and another twenty-one to a lesser extent. Should these be flooded, it has been calculated that, loss of life apart, material damage in excess of £1000 million would almost certainly be involved and London would not function properly for months.

The raising of banks has temporarily obviated any foreseeable disaster. After the 1928 floods, banks were raised, and again in 1971, but because of the sinking of the south-east, the risk is now greater than in pre-war days. It could be argued that bank raising could go on indefinitely, but what height would they be by, say, 2077? In the not too distant future, Londoners would be living in the shadow of great dykes canalizing their river: to view it they would have to mount the embankments. And what if such defences were breached?

A revolutionary approach was called for. It is now being implemented – the Thames Barrier.

As may be imagined, a great deal of consultation preceded the inauguration of such a scheme and many were the alternatives suggested. Perhaps the most ambitious was an enormous barrier stretching thirty miles across the outer estuary, from Margate to Clacton. But this would have taken twenty years to construct – too long – and its cost, estimated at the time of conception and therefore liable greatly to augment, would have been £10 000 million. This is not as ridiculous a proposition as that figure indicates. A great amount of land, notably in the Maplin area, would have been reclaimed. Further, no further costs on flood prevention on the Thames would have been incurred. But a crucial criticism of this proposal was its interference with shipping.

At the other extreme, a site by Cannon Street, in the City, was put forward. This would have been cheaper by far and offer no interference with shipping, but enormous bank raising would have been necessary downstream. There was much discussion between the shipping and docks interests, and the Greater London Council. Two sites were finally left in the running, Long Reach, by the Dartford Tunnel, a few miles upstream from Tilbury, and Woolwich Reach, which was the position finally chosen. Meanwhile, there was the question of what type of barrier should be built. The navigational interests naturally wanted the widest possible openings in the barrier; the G L C's engineers had to consider the practicalities of these demands. Just as the choice of Woolwich may be said to have been a matter of sensible British compromise, so was the decision to have a barrier with four 200-foot openings, two 100-foot openings and four of similar size for light vessels. Originally, drop gates were considered, but in order to clear the masts of 15 000 ton ships, the buildings supporting these would have had to be of colossal proportions, a series of massive mid-river skyscrapers. The exact opposite was decided on – a rising sector gate barrier. In this system

Artist's impression of the Thames Barrier currently under construction at Woolwich Reach. When completed in 1981 this will be the biggest movable barrier in the world. Closing the barrier, when required, will seal off part of the Tideway from the sea

the gates normally lie in casings housed on the river bed: one reason for preference for Woolwich Reach was the chalky and comparatively stable bed there. With rising gates, no overhead constructions are required and no impediment to normal navigation is involved, other than the piers between each opening, which house the machinery for raising the gates. The gates are pivoted so that they can be swung up in fifteen minutes. In the event of a critical surge tide, in short order a total barrier can be erected. This will be the biggest movable barrier in the world. Meanwhile downstream embankments are being raised where needed, and whilst industrial needs are not being overlooked, in residential areas the riverside defences will be landscaped and will add to the attractions of the river they tame.

The Thames Barrier should be complete by 1981.

It is thought it may then be necessary to raise it once or twice a year, perhaps only for practice. But it is estimated that fifty years from now it will probably be imperative to raise it ten times annually: that is why it is vital. The barrier itself will have no adverse effect on fish or birds. However, bank raising lower down may affect the habitat of some migratory birds and drive them down the estuary.

Brief thought had been given to a solid barrage, a dream of A. P. Herbert's to turn the London Thames into a tideless river. That would have killed London permanently as a port, and would have been industrially disastrous. A.P.H. was obsessed with the Thames as a haven for watermen: he was no engineer.

Another great project for the lower tidal Thames of which the completion may conceivably be seen by those now in their teens is a big deep water port at Maplin Sands, together with considerable land reclamation in that desolate area. Doubtless this will be vigorously contested by conservationists, though the idea is more commercially viable and infinitely less ecologically destructive than the (abandoned?) notion of placing an airport near by at Foulness.

There has also been put forward a scheme for an industrial-port complex in the Medway estuary, which caused a twenty-three-country international conservationist conference, plus UN representatives, to ask the British government to reject this idea.

But perhaps we are beginning to peer too far into the future. Where the Thames affects most people in the great conurbation of London, it is the activities of the Thames Water Authority which most obviously impinge on the general public. This is not to denigrate the important work of local councils, the G L C and the Port of London Authority: the division of responsibilities is complex, and I must necessarily write in rather broad terms.

The population of London proper is declining. However, this is largely compensated by migration to other locations within the Thames catchment area. Future planning must take this into account. Individual water use constantly rises, and this increases sewage and requirements for its treatment, if the Thames is to remain clean. Some sewers which have served the capital ably for a century and more are antiquated and must be reinforced or renewed. The demands on the Thames and Thames-side for recreational facilities continue to grow, and it is the intention of the Authority and all others concerned that these demands shall be met. There will be no slackening of the efforts that have seen such dramatic improvements in the river during the present reign, particularly in more recent years.

I feel the Authority can fully justify its own words that 'the services provided by Thames Water are the envy of most other parts of the world, including highly developed countries'.

The future is rosy for a Thames revivified, restored to old uses, transformed by fresh ones.

6 SUMMATION, ACKNOWLEDGEMENTS AND BIBLIOGRAPHY

Range all thy swans, fair Thames, together in a rank
And place them duly one by one upon the stately bank.

MICHAEL DRAYTON (1563-1631), *England's Helicon*

As a Londoner, it has been a most instructive pleasure to me to sketch this story (with a few digressions) of the transformation of the tidal Thames from infected and virtually lifeless concourse to healthy river.

As we have seen, many people, numerous organizations, industry, have played their parts in this rehabilitative success. So a great inheritance came to the Thames Water Authority on its inauguration in 1974, and that inheritance also conferred weighty responsibilities – some shared, some wholly its own. The Authority has reaped the kudos of the Thames triumph, a triumph for which honour must be paid to its predecessors, some now absorbed, some now its allies in consolidation of the victory over pollution. The battle has been won: its rewards can be seen. Fish in increasing abundance swim in waters they shunned twenty-five years ago and later. It is foreseeable that the water will again be 'as clear and pellucid as any such great river in the world', to quote a mid-seventeenth century writer. It is already superior to that of rivers serving most great cities.

Wild ducks fly and waders feed where formerly only the scavenging gulls found sustenance. Swans sail proudly on reaches that were so contaminated no bird could survive in them.

The Thames breathes again, as do its denizens, the citizens who live or work beside it, those who

R. Monti's statue of Father Thames at Cricklade, the lock nearest the river's source

practice leisure pursuits from banks or on the tide. These rewards are palpable and worth the effort and cost.

Yet the war goes on. Pollution – from technology, by flood, through nature herself – lurks ever ready to pounce. Congratulations are in order, providing they induce no over-confidence. From my researches I am convinced they will not. And that gives me cause to thank those who have helped in what had to be the rapid compilation of this publication. The only reward I can offer them is that, if the book achieves even modest success, they can say that without their aid I could not have undertaken it, let alone completed it.

Acknowledgements

My initial plunge into the subject of the cleansing of the Thames was guided by a lecture given at a symposium in Spokane, USA, by Mr Alex Morrison, Chief Executive, Thames Water. Once launched into the project, I, naturally enough, expected delay and obstruction from official bodies. In fact, I received promptness, efficiency, patience from every quarter I approached. So, in no particular order, I would like to record gratitude for direct assistance, in addition to textual references, to:

Mr Leslie Wood, Assistant Director, Pollution Control, Thames Water Authority, who steered me in good directions and gave me a most valuable interview and copies of important reports by him published by the GLC.

At Crossness, Mr Andrew Cockburn, of Thames Water, who handed me over to Mr Nigel Baker, who explained so lucidly to me the operation of this splendid sewage treatment plant, and to Mr Michael Andrews, marine biologist, who almost imbued me with his enthusiasm for fish.

Mr Ray Horner, Deputy Director, Department of Public Health Engineering, GLC, who introduced me to the mysteries of the Thames Barrier and tried to make me understand the meteorological principles of a surge tide.

Acknowledgements of indirect aid of a very useful kind are due to:

The organisers of the Effluent and Water Treatment Convention, Seymour Hall, London (1963) for sight of a paper 'Pollution of the Thames Valley during the Past Century', a brilliant condensation by Mr W. G. Barclay.

Mr P. R. A. Busby, Thames Water, who is in charge of sewage treatment for the London area, for his 1974 lecture on 'Evolution and Development of London's Main Drainage', given at the Institution of Electrical Engineers.

Books of Value

In the text I have referred to Mr Philip Howard's *London's River* (Hamish Hamilton, 1975, £6.50). This deals with the pollution of the Thames, the solution and future developments, but its special charm lies in the historical anecdotes. It is erudite, yet delightfully readable.

Likewise I have mentioned *The Thames Transformed* by Jeffrey Harrison and Peter Grant (André Deutsch, 1976, £5.95). In a foreword, the Duke of Edinburgh, ardent conservationist, sounds a word of caution against complacency. This book must be compulsive reading for ornithologists.

An excellent popular history of the Thames from Hampton Court to Greenwich is *London's Riverside* by Suzanne Ebel and Doreen Impney (William Luscombe, 1975, £6.95). It is also a very good guide to what is worth visiting beside the river – including the best pubs.

I found some background information in *Victorian London* by Priscilla Metcalf (Cassell, 1972, £2.75), a fine, short, well illustrated, study.

Probably more difficult than penning this book was the choosing of illustrations and planning the whole volume, and so I feel impelled to add sincere acknowledgements of the splendid work by the publishers' executives involved and by the public relations staff of Thames Water.

I can only trust that those who run through my synthesis of a big subject will discover an interest in it or find that a forgotten one is renewed, and may be encouraged to read deeper.

An enlightened public is the best reinforcement for those who serve the Thames.

Royal Borough of Kensington & Chelsea (on Thames), London, October – December 1976

INDEX

Italicized figures refer to illustrations on page cited.